Computerized Maintenance Management System

CMMS

Explained

2nd Edition made simple

Dave Bertolini

RELIABILITY
WEB.COM

Computerized Maintenance Management System
CMMS Explained
Made Simple - 2nd Edition

By Dave Bertolini

ISBN 978-1-941872-29-1

HF122018

Publisher: Reliabilityweb.com
Design and Layout: Apolonia Lemus

For information: Reliabilityweb.com
www.reliabilityweb.com
8991 Daniels Center Drive, Suite 105, Ft. Myers, FL 33912
Toll Free: 888-575-1245 | Phone: 239-333-2500
E-mail: crm@reliabilityweb.com

10   9   8   7

Table of Contents

Dedication

To my family: thanks for the years of support and understanding during all those missed anniversaries, birthdays, and special events in your lives…

Introduction

Let's start with the very basics and define what a CMMS is, a Computerized Maintenance Management System. It's a tool to assist in managing the maintenance function. It's **NOT** an accounting tool although it contains accounting functionality. I continue to subscribe that these systems should be considered a maintenance communication system. The original concept of these systems was to communicate throughout an organization. This communication was a direct result of utilizing work orders to initiate that communication. If that simple rule were followed, the information collected becomes a repository of reusable maintenance information that can guide an organization towards making factual and data-based decisions. This information should include at a minimum:

✓ Labor utilization (internal and external)
✓ Material usage
✓ Equipment repair history
✓ Repetitive failure identification
✓ Work procedures
✓ Key Performance Indicators (KPIs) or metrics
✓ Costing information for:
  - Labor
  - Materials
  - Equipment
  - Activities
  - Contractors

While it's important to understanding what the tool is, it's equally important to understand what it is not. It's not a "silver bullet." In actuality, it fixes nothing for you; however, it can indicate where your issues are. Remember you will only be able to get out of the system what you have put into the system.

These systems are not cheap; typical implementation costs range from seven to ten times the cost of the package. So a $100,000 system will ultimately cost $700,000 - $1,000,000 for full implementation.

These tools are not intuitive, so if you have never accomplished an implementation or re-implementation of a system, a word of caution: Get some implementation assistance and guidance.

These systems require training after implementation; the worst cost savings measure is to not provide training. You would be better off to save the money and not buy a system.

Do you really need one of these? Yes, if you...

✓ Have a budget and want to track expenditures against that budget
✓ Would like to develop a maintenance budget to the equipment level
✓ Want to understand, track, and manage the maintenance backlog
✓ Have maintenance work being accomplished at your site or facility
✓ Want to schedule maintenance activities to maximize craft utilization
✓ Want to prioritize that work so the critical equipment is serviced first
✓ Want to establish repeatable standards in the ways of working
✓ Have equipment that is under warranty
✓ Have parts or materials that are used in maintaining equipment
✓ Have projects that should be tracked
✓ Want to improve your maintenance performance based on data
✓ Want to establish performance measures
✓ Want to find ways to improve the organization
✓ Want to find the best place to spend the maintenance training budget

Although each system available processes and establishes data differently, there is enough commonality from data field to data field within them to generalize them for discussion points.

I will assume you have done the due diligence of identifying what your system needs are and have selected the appropriate system to meet those needs. Many organizations have never determined these needs and end up being saddled with a system that leaves users frustrated and disappointed. This ultimately leads to system stagnation (non-use) and failure. Remember the implemented cost of these systems. Can you really afford a potential $1,000,000 failure associated with you?

If you find yourself contemplating customizing aspects of your system, stop and rethink your implementation or re-implementation strategy. System customization can be expensive and system dependence may require re-customization with each future and subsequent system update.

The fastest, most efficient, and least expensive way to implement any system is in an "out of the box" configuration.

I continue to subscribe to the notion that there are no bad systems, only bad implementations coupled with poor utilizations of them. When unexpected circumstances occur during implementation (and they will), ensure training isn't canceled in an effort to save funds. As foolish as this may sound, it is a common occurrence made by many. Why establish a tool that no one understands how to utilize?

①
Why a 2ⁿᵈ Edition?

After the first edition was published, I knew there would be things that had been missed or just forgotten. Thanks to the readers of the first edition for your questions and comments. I enjoyed corresponding with you, and it motivated me to add more. This edition will hopefully provide those missing items, additional clarification, and more.

As before, the true target audience remains those who are implementing or re-implementing their systems. I encourage you to include the necessary resources from your organization and utilize the "do it with them" approach not the "do it to them approach." For those who are unsure of where their system is, I have included a system assessment to identify potential areas of improvement.

The overall goal is to make your system better and provide guidance to maximize your system and its informational value. The explanations of functionality are not from or for any particular system and are generic in nature, only because most, if not all, systems contain the functionality presented in this book.

Another area I noticed missing in the first edition was an explanation of terminology utilized in systems. It hit me one day after a conversation with a client that his understanding of a term used and the system's use of the term were vastly different. Something so simple was missing that could lead to disastrous results in an implementation, so I have included some of the typical terminology utilized in systems to help eliminate this issue.

Again, the intent is to identify the fundamentals that must be addressed for a successful implementation or re-implementation that yields useful information. There are other areas and functionalities of systems that could enhance your experience, but the goal is to educate you on the things that must be established for a solid foundation that you can continue building upon.

Since the first edition, I have predominately been working with one very large client assisting them in a re-implementation of their system. This organization is extremely broad in the scope of the products it manufactures and has numerous plants pretty much everywhere. One of the biggest lessons learned was the lack of defined standards throughout their enterprise. Numerous sites were left to "figure it out" on their own with little cross communication among like sites or across the different divisions within the company. There was a lack of what you will read in this book in place or in some circumstances even an understanding of why it's necessary.

Some of the things I encountered started from a basic misunderstanding of the functionality of their system and what systems overall can and should provide. This book was utilized to develop a system overview training program to educate and establish a foundation of system knowledge with them. The refreshing reward was hearing at almost every session "if someone had only told me that before."

The lack of documented standards bit us numerous times during the project: something as simple as establishing an equipment type for a motor resulted in the discovery of more than 30 unique equipment types for motors. Upon further system review, it was discovered there were over 4,000 unique equipment types. Now that standards have been established, there are less than 400 unique equipment types across their enterprise. The concepts and ideas presented in this book have been utilized and are proven; it's up to you to utilize them.

One final plea to get it right. The most exciting system-related job I have worked was for a large law firm. The scope of the work was to review the system data and determine if the involved sites were maintained utilizing the principles of Best Practices. The scope further specified analysis, documentation of the results, and attending the Grand Jury hearing as the testifying expert. After my findings were documented and delivered, I was later notified that the case would be settled out of court for hundreds of millions of dollars. The big lesson learned here is how comfortable are you utilizing your systems data to defend yourself in court?

Enjoy reading, and hopefully the answers you are looking for are contained within these pages, if you feel you need amplification on specific areas or concepts let me know.

② What's All the Hype About?

These systems are not new to the maintenance world. In fact, they have been available for over forty years in varying price ranges, industries, and configurations. If you do a quick internet search for "CMMS," you get 645,000 results. These results range from those selling systems to explanations of what they are. There are the top 10 system listings, systems specific to industries, cloud based systems, and even free systems. The diligence of identifying and utilizing the appropriate system to meet your organizational needs is one of your bigger challenges. Ironically, these systems can, in fact, do everything they say they can do **IF** implemented and utilized correctly.

A common misconception is that a CMMS is typically designed and utilized in and for small organizations. While I have seen them utilized in small facilities and single manufacturing environments, I have also seen them utilized in large environments supporting 100 plants in enterprise type applications. Size really doesn't matter; implementation and utilization do.

Think back to when you sat through the system demonstration when you were buying your system: the seamless movement through the system and the abundance of information that was available when you moved from screen to screen. Look at your system now: seamless and with an abundance of information or clunky and empty? Seamless and abundant' please forward your resume; clunky and empty, please continue reading…

Most view these systems as merely a means to schedule maintenance work. While this may be driven by one's understanding of a system, it is far from the correct view of a system or the typical capabilities of these systems. With the integration of all equipment data, parts, and people to provide support, significant information can be available quickly, provided it is entered. A majority of work accomplished by a maintenance organization can be managed through any system, provided the system is implemented correctly and utilized properly. Welcome to the first opportunity to provide disappointment: the failure to provide the necessary data coupled with a lack of understanding system capabilities.

Show Me the Money

I'm often asked what the Return on Investment (ROI) is for having a system. I have seen software vendors offer ROI calculators that assist in determining any, but that makes an assumption that the system is implemented and utilized correctly. It's apparent that by making people more effective and efficient, there is a cost saving, but how do you put your arms around it?

One of the better tools I have found is from the Association of Facilities Engineers (AFE). It requires you to look at what your maintenance resources are doing and the time it takes them. While 100% is not a direct result of having a system, a significant majority of it is (perhaps as much as 90%). Utilize a typical maintenance resource in a typical day at your site to understand the cost associated with ineffectiveness.

The Cost of Ineffectiveness

The first measure (1) looks at time spent looking for parts, perhaps wandering the storeroom or thumbing through a printed copy listing of all inventory in stock. Just the time spent trying to identify required parts or materials is extremely time consuming in an unmanned storeroom environment. This activity is often referred to as "maintenance shopping time."

The second measure (2) looks at time spent trying to understand what work you want them to accomplish. Perhaps the work order says "fix the pump," so research is necessary to identify what must be done or even where it may be located. Tools or parts may be required, which could cause multiple trips to the shop or storeroom trying to obtain information or clarification of what must be done.

The third measure (3) looks at time spent starting one job, but before completion the individual gets pulled off for another job deemed more important, which may or may not actually be. Of course, while this happens little or no work is fully completed.

The last measure (4) looks at the time spent waiting for the equipment to be available. The equipment was scheduled for a quarterly PM; however, when maintenance arrives, the operator says to wait an hour because it wasn't known that maintenance was required, or at least not required today. Being a maintenance guy myself, I know we are fascinated by watching equipment operate, so we watch it for the hour. Again, think of your typical maintenance resource in their typical day, ask them or observe them with the following chart (Figure 1).

	The Measure	Average Time (Daily %)	Comments
1	The time spent looking for parts or materials to execute a maintenance activity?	% of day	The amount of time maintenance resources spend looking for needed parts.
2	Time spent looking for necessary work order information to execute a maintenance activity?	% of day	The amount of time spent researching information.
3	Time wasted by starting the wrong priority work?	% of day	The amount of time spent starting a job and before completion pulling the maintenance resource off to respond to another activity.
4	Time spent waiting for the equipment to become available to execute a maintenance activity?	% of day	The amount of time waiting for the equipment to become available or released to start an activity.
5	Enter the total of lines 1 – 4		The total of the average amount of time a typical maintenance resource loses in a day.
6	Enter the number of total maintenance resources		The total maintenance work force available to execute maintenance activities.
7	Multiple the total of line 6 X 2080		The total hours the maintenance work force has available to execute maintenance activities (assumes 2,080 hours per year).
8	Multiple line 5 X line 7		Annual total maintenance hours lost due to ineffectiveness or inefficiencies.
9	Average maintenance resource burdened labor rate		Total hourly maintenance employee cost (with benefits & fringe).
10	Multiple line 8 X line 9		Total annual labor expenditure.
11	Multiple line 10 X 25%		The financial saving by a 25% reduction in ineffectiveness.
12	Multiple line 10 X 40%		The financial saving by a 40% reduction in ineffectiveness.

Figure 1: Cost of Ineffectiveness

Let's look at the results. Because of the inherent and sometimes unknown inefficiencies associated with maintenance, these measures can only be improved 25% - 40%, but that can be significant. What does all this really have to do with a CMMS?

These measures can easily be improved with a properly implemented system that quickly provides all necessary information for the materials within the storeroom. Item descriptions, locations, and quantities on hand are known and quickly identifiable eliminating the "maintenance shopping time" time. Because of the processes and flows, you have defined the scope of work, the necessary tools, and materials as a result of the work order planning effort. Work priorities and equipment criticalities would be established as part of the overall work management process and the important work would be known. Waiting for equipment availability can be reduced by developing maintenance schedules in advance and sharing them with the organization. There is a Return on Investment for having a system; you just have to determine what yours is.

The common theme among systems is the collection of costing information (labor and materials) through utilization of the system. Another common theme is the automation of workflows and processes which establish repeatable standards. But, unfortunately for many, this is yet another stumble made during implementation. This automation regrettably is not total automation and requires manual user intervention at varying points. This intervention normally comes from completing specific actions or a series of actions within the system. While some actions can be automated, they are typically limited to approvals and notifications that further action(s) is/are required. Processing a work orders through its lifecycle (creation to closure) is a great example. Various roles within the organization must review, approve, and select an appropriate action to move the work order along its route from when it was created to when it is completed.

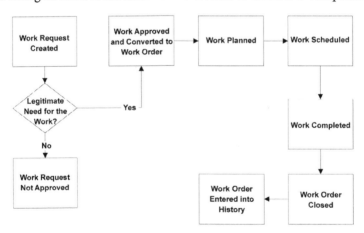

Figure 2: Basic Work Order Flow

Each specific block, as illustrated in Figure 2, represents an intervention or user action required to move it through the system (the work order lifecycle). Many understand this flow and most systems utilize this as the work management basis. However, this level is unacceptable for true work management and must be further defined and broken down into logical steps. I have found the best way to start is develop a list of what workflows and processes must be developed and then utilize a program like Microsoft Visio® to further define and document them.

These flows will become critical to you in the future when you are defining your system statuses and when those statuses must be applied. The defining of system statuses will be discussed in the work order section. These workflows and processes should become part of the Standard Operating Procedure (SOP) document you will be developing and utilizing as the foundation for your future system training program.

Basic fundamental flows must include:

The Work Management Process
- Work identification
- Work approval
- Work planning
- Work scheduling
- Work execution
- Work closeout
- Work history
- Reporting and Metrics

Materials Management Process
- Reserving inventory (allocation)
- Ordering stocked items
- Ordering non-stocked items
- Parts kitting
- Inventory de-allocation
- Issuing inventory
- Inventory counting (physical or cycle)

Maintenance or Reliability Engineering Process
- Failure reporting
- Equipment historical reviews

There may be other flows and processes that you'll define based on the nature of your business and the level at which you plan to implement and ultimately utilize your system.

Historically, users of these systems utilize thirty percent or less of the inherent capabilities of their system. I have encountered countless organizations that have been content with this low level of utilization. This has always bothered me, if you bought it all, why not use it all? Some of this is attributed to a lack of understanding of what your system can do, while some is attributed to a lack of time to complete the implementation properly.

The main purpose of these systems is to accurately track activities based upon the type of activity being accomplished, where it's being accomplished, who is accomplishing it, how long it took to accomplish, and what was the cost of accomplishing it. Just by that simple statement, you can quickly see where numerous things must be defined and ultimately established within the system to provide you with the necessary information you're looking for.

To enable the tracking of the types of activities being accomplished, work order types must be defined (work order types will be discussed in the work order section). Also to enable tracking, the person(s) who is accomplishing the activity for the crafts and internal/external labor must be defined (crafts and labor will be discussed in the labor section). When we think of time to accomplish an activity, we typically focus on the "wrench time." But what about the time to get it through the process? Mean time to approve a work order, mean time to plan the work order, and mean time to execute the work all could be valuable to you to validate the established process or improve upon it.

Remember, if left unmonitored, your system can and will be viewed as a "void." If work requests are left in an "unapproved" status for extended periods of time, those that entered them become frustrated and eventually stop entering future work. The lack of action or perceived lack of action is a large contributor to data disappointment.

The costing aspect is simple, provided you establish labor rates, material costs and accomplish all work with a work order that has been written to a specific piece of equipment or an asset. The standard rule of thumb for all systems is no work order written... no event ever happened. To ensure all necessary information is collected for future data harvesting, a culture of discipline must be established that reinforces a "no work order, no work" policy. The same holds true for the issue of materials, which must be issued to the work order or directly to the equipment or asset. Obviously, in the event of emergency or urgent work, the work order can be entered after the event. The key is to ensure the information gets entered for future analysis and reporting.

There are numerous decisions that must be made to properly implement or re-implement a system. To fully understand them is critical to your system's success. The basic guidelines and rational for those decisions are contained in the remainder of this book. I encourage you to read the entire book before attempting to apply them and seek guidance if you do not understand them. Good luck: your people are counting on you.

Lessons from Around the
Campfire at Consultants Camp

Through years of implementing these systems, I've seen good system implementations, bad system implementations, and some that left me shaking my head as I walked away. Conducting a system re-implementation is expensive; however, it's still faster and cheaper than starting over and purchasing another system.

- When you ask people about their system, you typically learn their current system isn't as good as their previous system, but their next system will be better.

- There are two types of users: users of the system and users of the information. Unfortunately, most organizations concentrate on the user of the information and forget about the user of the system. If you make it simple for the user of the system to provide required information, there will always be information within the system. If not, prepare yourself for disappointment.

- Determine your system needs for today and twenty years from today. Educate yourself on Best Practices, specifically maintenance Best Practices. Since you are implementing a Computerized Maintenance Management System, you must ensure the necessary maintenance data needs will be met and established within the system; after all, it is a maintenance tool.

- Remember these systems are not cheap. If you buy it all, use it all. Maximize the utilization of the system capabilities. Establish the basics and build upon that.

- Ensure you fully understand the system definition of each field. Many implementations have disappointed users simply because of differences or a lack of understanding the system's intent from the user's intent.

- With the exception of the narrative text contained within tasks, all entries should be in CAPITAL LETTERS. This removes any confusion of determining if it's a letter or a number. Those weary eyes at 3:00 a.m. really do appreciate that.

- Document all implementation decisions, workflows, and processes in a Standard Operating Procedure (SOP) document. Provide each user a copy of this document for future and on-going reference. Have copies available to provide to new employees and utilize them as part of their on-board training.

- When possible, avoid using abbreviations in field labels and data table headings. If the entire word will fit, enter it. This will minimize any confusion about an abbreviation. If an abbreviation must be utilized, make sure it is documented in the Standard Operating Procedures document and fully entered in the description field associated with that table.

- Avoid using a space in a key field, for example an equipment number of AB 12345, should be entered as AB-12345. It's easy to put two spaces and never realize it, so AB 12345 and AB 12345 could both be established as equipment or asset numbers.

- If possible, avoid using I's and O's as lead letters for equipment numbering or other key data fields. It clears the confusion up on I, O, 1, or 0 for the system user.

- User Defined Fields (UDF) are handy for the storage of temporary data; however, in most systems these fields are free text fields and are not validated tables. This presents the opportunity to insert information that data standards cannot be applied to, and we all know how we spel, speil, spell...

- Consider making a majority of the validated fields within the system "read only" so only a few have access to make changes. This helps maintain configuration control of tables and data fields. Ensure you have identified the appropriate role(s) to make changes when they become necessary.

- Leave nothing to personal interpretation; if it can be utilized wrong, it will be utilized wrong.

- If you make it difficult to establish information within the system, you will never get information within the system.

- Pictures are worth a thousand words, so take advantage of attaching or linking pictures, additional documents, specifications, etc. If it makes it easier to accomplish a task more safely, more efficiently, and more effectively, then why not include them? Just remember, when attaching items, it must be on a location where the users can access it and your computer's hard drive will not work.

- Failure to provide adequate system training leads to data gaps, misinformation, frustration, and ultimately, a chorus of "the system is not-user-friendly." I always question something deemed "not user-friendly" as a potential training issue. Remember, training must go beyond the classroom and include on the floor coaching and mentoring. Bad habits left uncorrected become common habits.

- When establishing work order numbering, consider utilizing a two digit year identifier as the prefix (i.e.15-000001). This provides a quick reference to identify old work orders within the system. Many, but not all, systems have this configurable option. If established, don't forget to change the prefix at the start of the new year.

- Remember the people who will be utilizing your system:

  - Some are convinced computers will never catch on...
  - Some feel "it's the man's way of watching me"...
  - Some are too busy to ever attend training...
  - Some have never used a computer before...
  - Some can't read or write...
  - Some believe computers contain voodoo and black magic powers...
  - Some think they are actually smarter than any program could ever be, especially your program...

- Paint the picture for each user on what the benefit is for them. We all want to know "what's in it for me" if I use this thing? If you can't tell them, chances are you're not going to get them to use it, and ultimately, you're not going to get the data you desire.

- Never utilize system information for evil purposes, or you will only receive misinformation in return.

- Most times what is viewed as a system error is in fact exactly what you asked the system to do, you just didn't like the results. Or a couple IT terms that I recently learned:

  - There appears to be a short between the seat and the keyboard
  - That's a PICNIC... Problem In Chair Not In Computer

4

Implementation Made Simple

When I first started implementing systems for organizations, the approach was straight forward and simple. I would show up, have some quick discussions with the organization, develop some fundamental workflows and processes, build the equipment hierarchy, populate all required data fields within the system, and train a site individual on what had been accomplished. After I left, no one remembered what was done, why it was done, or how it was done. Then I realized this was providing a disservice not a service because no transfer of knowledge ever occurred.

I reevaluated my implementation approach and moved to a coaching and mentoring role, or as previous clients have told me, "an adult supervision" role. To me, this was that "enlightened" moment; this approach assured a transfer of knowledge and, as I later learned, instilled site ownership of the system long after my involvement. Figure 3 shows the sequence of implementation events that should be followed when attempting an implementation or re-implementation of a system:

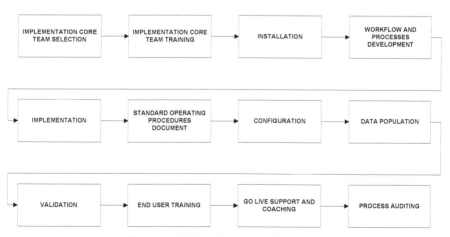

Figure 3: CMMS Sequence of Events

Building the Team

The Implementation Core Team is the identification and selection of a cross-functional team (maintenance, operations, materials management, information technologies, maintenance and operational planners, accounting/purchasing and management). Some push back on this and respond with "they don't know anything about systems," but they will when the task is complete. This is the bulk of your implementation workforce and although it will not be necessary to utilize one hundred percent of each team member's time, it is critical to ensure ample time is dedicated to accomplish implementation or re-implementation activities. This must be a cross-functional team to ensure each unique role's utilization, input, and output aspects are understood and established within the system. These individuals will become your site's system experts and future trainers for your organization. This keeps the knowledge in house.

Training the Team

Core team training is overview training of the system and its capabilities to the implementation core team to ensure system capabilities are understood. This training is typically conducted by the system vendor at your site. This will lay the framework for "training the trainers" while ensuring all system capabilities have been seen, understood and can be implemented to their fullest extent. Once accomplished, this paints the "picture" of the system to the team and ensures system intended use and site intended use are aligned.

Installing the Package

Installation is the physical installation of the system on the network. If accomplishing a new system implementation at this point, the system is void of any site data. If accomplishing a re-implementation, some or all data may be removed from the system. In my experience, it was often more efficient to start with a clean installation for most re-implementations. Installation is typically accomplished with the site IT department and the implementation core team.

Defining How It Works

Workflows and process define how the system will be utilized along with the flow of data to ensure standardization in system utilization and system data collection. This often overlooked critical phase is the cause of many system implementation failures. The purpose of workflow and process development is to ensure repeatable standards are established, understood by all users, adhered to, and periodically audited. These flows and processes must be trained to the entire organization to ensure valid data is collected for future data harvesting. It is extremely important that the utilization of the system is seamlessly blended into everyday use; if processes or required procedures are difficult or cumbersome to follow, they will not be followed.

Defining Data Standards

Implementation is the defining phase to develop all pertinent data standards that ensure consistent data collection. This is where serious consideration should be given to soliciting outside help to guide the implementation core team. Most systems by nature are neither intuitive nor simple to understand. Here's where an experienced system implementer working with the core team can be invaluable ensuring you understand the decisions you are making and the ramifications of those decisions. This is definitely a great place for the old adage, "you don't know what you don't know." Another word of caution, choose your implementation help wisely. Although the vendor you purchased the system from may offer implementation services, it has been my experience that vendors know their system well but typically lack a maintenance *Best Practices* background.

Leaving a Legacy

The development of a Standard Operating Procedure (SOP) is the team's legacy when the implementation is complete. This documenting phase captures all definitions developed during the implementation phase. Each system area and each field definition must be documented within the SOP for future reference. It is not uncommon to have five hundred to nine hundred or more decisions documented at the completion of this phase. I have always viewed this document as the implementation legacy left for others to understand the established who, what, and how of the system. Templates for the data collection of equipment, materials, tools, and employees should be developed and included in this document. This becomes the foundation for system training for current and future system users.

Configuring the System

Configuration is the establishment within the system of all those standards defined during the implementation phase and documented in the Standard Operating Procedures document. The implementation core team establishes each definition in the proper field and/or table within the system. My experience during system configuration has shown that dividing the implementation core team into assignments for each system area works best. Once the assignments are made, they should be completed by those assigned to ensure data entry consistency and established data standards are followed. Ensure adequate time is given to complete these activities; it's much better to get it completed accurately than to get it completed quickly.

Putting It All Together

Data population is the population of site data, such as employees, equipment, materials, etc. This data is typically in numerous formats and locations throughout the site. Serious consideration should be given to migrating data from one system to another. Most times, migrating data is costly, time consuming, and normally yields little value. If you are considering migrating transactional data (work order history, inventory transactions, etc.), serious thought should be given to the value of that data. You are re-implementing the system for a reason, so how valuable or accurate can that data be? Templates that were defined and documented in the SOP should be utilized for the collection of all data that must be populated. It is critical these templates are utilized to ensure all necessary data standards are followed when the data is collected. Data collection and population are two of the most time-consuming and expensive efforts; therefore, it is imperative that only necessary and standardized data is collected.

Getting It Right

Validation is a final system review of all data to ensure future data harvesting opportunities exist. This validation effort is focused on several main areas to ensure accuracy and completeness of the core data (equipment, materials, labor, and accounting information). Thorough testing of the procedures and processes developed to support the maintenance function and system functionality is conducted, and corrections are made as necessary.

A plan to capture the existing transactional and accounting data necessary to complete the month-end and year-end accounting must be developed if re-implementing a system currently in use. The last item is often overlooked and the amount of effort is often underestimated. Many maintenance transactions take place over the course of months. Development of a test and validation plan to transition these transactions in progress from the existing system into the new system is critical to ensure minimum impact to the business.

Training the Masses

End user training is the training for all site users based on their respective roles within the organization. This training utilizes all documents developed during the implementation and is conducted by the on-site system experts (the implementation core team). Be sure training starts with the established workflows and processes. If these are not understood by the site, nothing will flow through the system properly. System training must be conducted by user roles (maintenance resources, planners, materials management, etc.). It makes little sense to train on areas or system functions that will never be used by a specific role. Remember, each user must receive training and casual users typically need follow-up coaching or training. This is the opportunity to give each user a copy of the Standard Operating Procedures document that was developed.

Going Live

Go live support/coaching is that on the floor support and coaching provided by the implementation core team to ensure the workflows, processes and system utilization are performed properly. This accelerates the learning on the floor as well as gets users acquainted with the proper system use while reinforcing the training received. Remember, if allowed to use the system incorrectly from the start, it will always be utilized incorrectly. Stop bad habits before they become common practice.

Auditing for Success

Process auditing is a defined audit to ensure consistent data standards are followed and workflows and process improvement opportunities are identified. Periodic audits must be performed on the workflows, processes, and system utilization. Audits should be performed immediately after the system goes live to ensure bad habits are not allowed and desired data is being collected.

Causes of Failures and Data Disappointments

Now would be the appropriate time to talk about the causes of system implementation failures. If the statistics thrown around are close to correct, there appears to be a high implementation failure rate (up to ninety percent). How is that possible for a tool that has been around for nearly forty years? Simple, you don't know what you don't know. I'm a firm believer that if you understand the causes of failure, you can avoid failure. Here are some of the main causes of failures typically encountered:

Not understanding or underestimating the scope of the effort:
- Insufficient level of talent assigned
- Insufficient labor availability
- Insufficient budget established
- Insufficient or unrealistic timeline established
- Cross-functional team not utilized

Lack of management support:
- Inadequate or no commitment of labor resources
- Inadequate capital allocation
- Inadequate visible support
- Inadequate or no training commitment

Poor or no workflow or processes defined:
- No plan to integrate the system with day-to-day activities
- Reactive attitude, can't think in a proactive mode
- System never put in the hands of the true end users

Not following the CMMS sequence of events:
- Critical implementation areas not addressed
- Not understanding system capabilities
- Lack of site level ownership
- Lack of on-site system experts

Wrong or inappropriate system:
- System will not support site data needs
- All necessary modules not purchased or implemented
- Inadequate amount of user licenses (system availability)

To ensure you avoid failure, develop a plan to implement or re-implement the system. Follow a proven methodology or sequence of events, get the appropriate stakeholders involved in the implementation, and provide the proper level of assistance and support. Review the section again on what these systems are not: Remember the "not cheap" discussion? Avoid failure at all costs; mistakes are expensive and time consuming to correct.

Understanding System Functionality

Each module or area of a CMMS contains multiple data fields that must be defined and eventually populated with data to make the system function properly. Typical modules or areas found in most systems are employees or labor, equipment, materials management, purchasing, preventive and predictive maintenance or tasks, work orders, system security, and reporting and analysis. Although many systems have additional modules or areas, these are the critical ones that must be addressed. Normally, additional features or functionality require these modules or areas to be defined and populated first.

Figure 4 depicts a typical order or sequence of implementation events by module or area of a system. Following this flow will save time while ensuring all applicable areas are addressed.

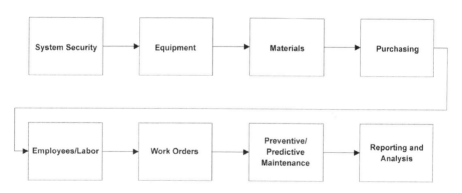

Figure 4: Sequence of Implementation

System Security

Security is established to control access to the configuration elements of the system. Roles are created to allow access to menus, forms, field levels, and table levels. Users are created and assigned to a specific role based on their level of system access required. Typically, this is one of the first activities accomplished during implementation. You are preparing to enter a significant amount of data and want to protect the access immediately to ensure rework is not necessary. The most efficient way to assign security is by user roles. This will require you to identify all roles within the organization and define what specific area(s) of the system they will normally utilize. Typical roles could be management, supervisors, maintenance planner, maintenance crafts, operations or production, buyers, materials management, human resources, and reliability or maintenance engineering. The goal is to develop the appropriate organizational roles; however, they should be general and limited to as few roles as necessary. Each user of the system would be assigned to a specified role. This is much more efficient than developing security for each user. You may find it helpful to develop a matrix (see Figure 5) to assist in defining system roles.

SYSTEM ROLE	SYSTEM ACCESS							
	SYSTEM SECURITY	EQUIPMENT	MATERIALS	PURCHASING	EMPLOYEES	WORK ORDERS	PREVENTIVE PREDICTIVE MAINTENANCE	REPORTING & ANALYSIS
SYSTEM ADMINISTRATOR	X	X	X	X	X	X	X	X
MANAGEMENT		X	X	X		X	X	X
SUPERVISOR (MAINTENANCE)		X	X	X	X	X		X
MAINTENANCE PLANNER		X	X	X	X	X	X	X
SUPERVISOR (PRODUCTION)		X	X	X		X		X
MAINTENANCE CRAFTS		X	X			X		X
PRODUCTION		X				X		
BUYERS		X	X	X				X
MATERIALS MANAGEMENT		X	X	X		X		X
HUMAN RESOURCES					X			X
RELIABILITY ENGINEERING		X	X			X	X	X

Figure 5: System Role Assignment Matrix

Once roles are defined, security is then applied to each specific role. Security is typically which module or area, which fields within a module or area may accept input, may be read only, or may be hidden altogether. When a field is "hidden," only those with full access will see any information contained within those fields. Most systems (by default) give the System Administrator role full access to everything within the system. The System Administrator role may be a collateral role assigned to an individual. This individual should not perform their primary role in the System Administrator log in. Again, I have found the use of a matrix (see Figure 6) helpful.

EQUIPMENT Module/Area	SYSTEM ROLE							
	SYSTEM ADMINISTRATOR	MANAGEMENT	SUPERVISOR (MAINTENANCE)	MAINTENANCE PLANNER	SUPERVISOR (PRODUCTION)	MAINTENANCE CRAFTS	PRODUCTION	BUYERS
EQUIPMENT NUMBER	FA	RO	RO	FA	RO	RO	RO	RO
EQUIPMENT DESCRIPTION	FA	RO	RO	FA	RO	RO	RO	RO
LOCATION	FA	RO	RO	FA	RO	RO	RO	RO
CRITICALITY	FA	RO	RO	FA	RO	RO	RO	RO
DEPARTMENT	FA	RO	RO	FA	RO	RO	RO	RO
EQUIPMENT TYPE	FA	RO	RO	FA	RO	RO	RO	RO
GENERAL LEDGER	FA	RO	RO	RO	HN	HN	HN	FO
FA = Full Access								
RO = Read Only								
HN = Hidden								

Figure 6: System Security Assignment by Role

This simple matrix is not comprehensive, so you must define it based on your system. Each field within an area or module of the system must be identified and established. Additionally, I have found it beneficial to include the completed matrix within the Standard Operating Procedures document for user reference. This quickly identifies which roles have access to which areas for data needs.

Equipment

The equipment module or area should contain <u>all data</u> for each maintainable piece of equipment or asset contained within the site. This module or area is the most critical of the system since it contains the equipment hierarchy, which is considered the "backbone" of the system. The hierarchy requires significant thought and must include a top down approach starting with the site itself. I have found it helpful to follow the process flow of the site. Identify the site, the functional locations, the systems, and then the equipment.

One of the biggest contributors to data disappointment in a CMMS is an incomplete or inaccurate equipment/asset hierarchy. The hierarchy establishes the structure for numerous aspects of system functionality. A majority of these disappointments can be corrected with a properly defined hierarchy utilizing an internationally recognized equipment taxonomy or natural grouping of equipment.

It's all about the parent child relationships established that enable; cost roll-ups, equipment/asset identification, data analysis, reporting for metrics, and failure threads (MTBF, Failure Rates, etc.). Typical hierarchies are routinely void of all site assets, lack defined parent child relationships, and many times lack logical flow. Organizations must manage their assets and using accurate equipment taxonomy is a requirement.

Once the functional location of the area and the sub functions are identified the equipment/assets can be inserted and established with its respective parent. All maintainable equipment/assets should be identified and/or those that have a defined maintenance strategy. For example a functional location of "Press In-Feed" has the following equipment associated with it. A roller conveyor, an electric motor, a gearbox, and a VFD (Variable Frequency Drive).

Start at highest level required for your organization and define the hierarchy (sometimes referred as the functional location) down to the component or maintainable item level. What are the functions? Let's say we define an "Equipment Unit" as "Press #1" and one of its sub units is "Hydraulic System", "Electric Motors" are one of the type components/maintainable items in this system. The lowest level could be utilized to attach Bill of Material (BOM) information. The hierarchy structure would be represented as shown using Equipment Taxonomy (natural grouping of equipment).

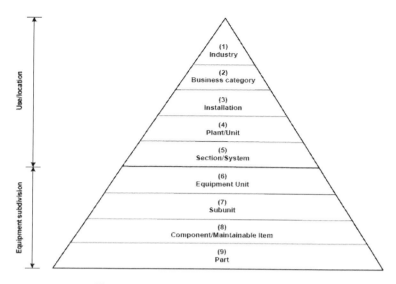

Figure 7: Equipment Taxonomy Example

Using the equipment taxonomy example shown above (Figure 7), one can identify similar failure issues on all "Electric Motors" for the assets at "Plant A" or within specific "Areas". Mean Time Between Failure (MTBF) for all electric motors in "Plant A" or electric motor or motors on the "Hydraulic System" could now be quickly obtained. Once the hierarchy is accurate and aligned utilizing equipment taxonomy then MTBF, Failure Rate, Cost, effectiveness of the maintenance strategy, etc. can be identified with a few key strokes of the computer.

Identifying what is causing the majority of any type component or maintainable item failures begins with knowing that you have a problem. The graphs on page 28 show the MTBF of over 500 electric motors (50-500 horsepower) at one site and how one Reliability Engineer made adjustments to the maintenance strategy (lubrication and alignment) which impacted MTBF in a positive direction along with reducing cost for new motors and the rebuilding of motors. This is just one example for why the equipment hierarchy must be established utilizing a standard to optimize asset reliability and cost.

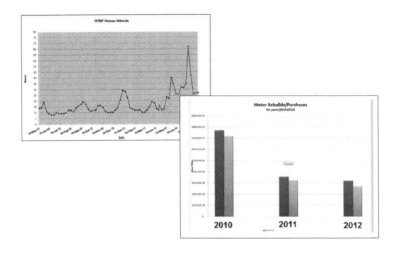

An assessment of a CMMS should be performed to ensure your current system has standardized equipment descriptions, equipment types and classes, and functional locational data. Once completed a walk-down validation should be performed to ensure all assets are included in the system.

Getting this correct enhances the capabilities and functionality of the system and eliminates data disappointment.

A functional location may mirror what you call departments; systems may mirror what you call lines or areas. If you think about Utilities you might consider that a system, however, if you consider Utilities as a functional location, then the logical "systems" could be water, heat and air, compressed air, etc., for example: ABC (Site), UTILITIES (Functional Location), COMPRESSED AIR (System), and AIR COMPRESSOR #1 (Equipment), see Figure 8.

If established incorrectly, roll-up (vertical) and comparison (horizontal) searching, sorting, and reporting will not possible. Spend the necessary time to get this part right, or everything in the system will be dysfunctional. I have found it best to conduct this activity with the implementation core team, a large dry erase board, and multiple walks through the site to ensure everything is identified and ultimately established.

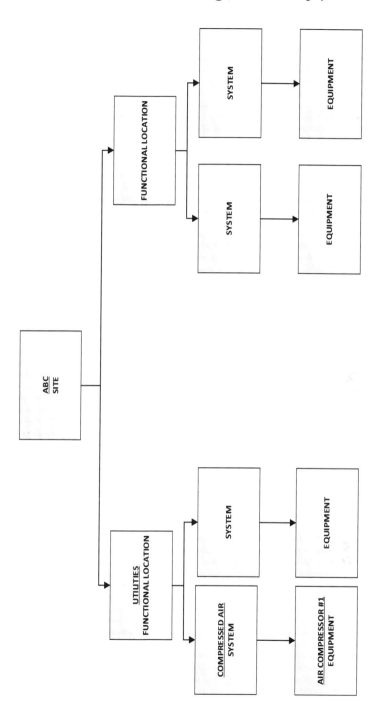

Figure 8: Functional Location Example

Equipment Hierarchy Example

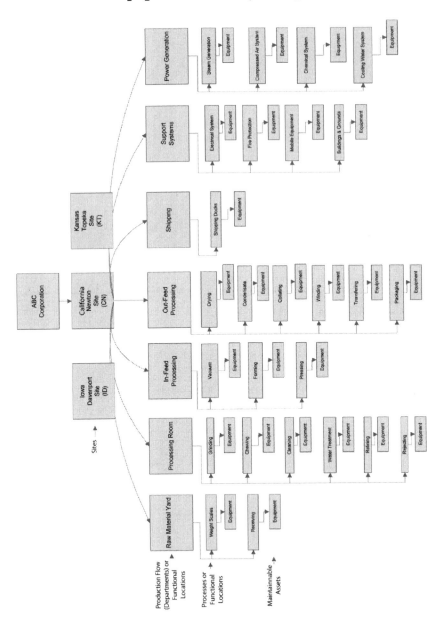

Figure 9: A High Level Multiple Site Hierarchy

Typical items that must be defined are a unique equipment number, a well-structured description, equipment type or classification (or sometimes both), location, cost center, department, warranty information, links to Bill of Material (BOM) information, etc. The equipment module or area is one of the most information intensive to populate, so a well-defined informational gathering process must be established to ensure only necessary information is collected. I have found that if the process flow (in a manufacturing environment) is followed, the end users can quickly relate to navigating the hierarchy. It is imperative that all understand how to locate a specific piece of equipment or asset, so historical information is collected to that specific piece of equipment or asset. It should be the exception that work orders are written to the department or process level. Keep in mind there are always exceptions to exceptions, i.e., an example of a valid work order written to the process level could be a visual inspection of the entire line or process.

Parent–Child Relationships

A parent is an asset to which other assets are assigned or "linked." For area type assets, this could be considered a functional location. For equipment assets, this could be the area in which it is located or a larger piece of equipment that it is a part of. Using the hierarchy example, the RAW MATERIAL YARD (functional location) would be the parent of the WEIGHT SCALES (equipment or asset).

The assets assigned to a parent asset are known as child assets or children. Using the same hierarchy example, the WEIGHT SCALES is a child of the RAW MATERIAL YARD. The parent/child relationship is a way of assigning component assets (children) to larger, all-inclusive assets (parents). An unlimited number of parent/child relationships between assets can normally be defined. Even though a child can only have one parent, a parent can have multiple children, and these children can also be parents of child assets.

Equipment Numbering

More heated discussions and debates have been started over defining an equipment numbering scheme for inclusion into systems than any other system decision. I have always thought of the equipment number merely as a unique identifier, much like your taxpayer identification number that only identifies you as an individual. The key is no two numbers are the same in either a system or a taxpayer identification number. Some systems have the capabilities to automatically assign numbering, while others require the user to assign the numbering. In the event your system requires the user to assign numbering, someone must be designated to maintain the master list of available numbers for future use.

Many like to invent a "smart numbering" scheme (see Figure 10) where a number or series of numbers represent aspects of the equipment, process, system, or even a location. This is unnecessary since most of those aspects are fields within a typical system that would enhance search and sort capabilities if populated. I have always subscribed to the idea: after the "smart ones" are gone, no one remembers the rational of the smart numbering scheme.

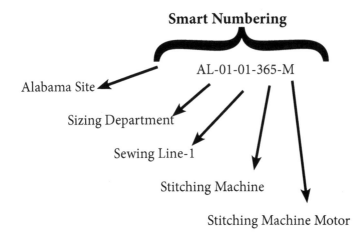

Figure 10: Smart Numbering Example

System dependent, you may have to develop specific identifiers if you're in a multiple plant or site environment (see Figure 9 i.e. ID, CN, KT) to ensure there are no duplicate equipment numbers across the enterprise.

Regardless of what you ultimately define as a numbering scheme, if you do not tag the equipment with the number established within the system, you can never be assured the correct piece of equipment was identified or ultimately worked on. Equipment tags are available in numerous types of material for virtually any equipment operating environment, and this ensures better accuracy in equipment identification. Each tag should contain the equipment or asset number and its description as contained within the system.

A final thought on equipment numbers: When an asset is removed from service, many systems will not allow you to remove the asset from the system, specifically if cost accounting data is contained in the history. I have found that if an asset is dismantled from the hierarchy (removed from its parent asset), annotated that it has been removed from service, and the equipment number has a "Z" placed in front (Z-12345), it can be forced to the bottom of all equipment listings or reports. Changing the equipment number in most systems will change all associated records in history as well. This may be an activity the System Administrator must accomplish. Additionally, reports can be modified to exclude any equipment number starting with "Z" to ensure these will not be seen.

Equipment Description

Working hand-in-hand with the equipment number is the equipment description. Typically, site or facility personnel know the equipment by a number or name. To ensure accurate data collection occurs, consider tagging all equipment or assets identified within the system with both the equipment number and the description. Standardization is important, so a well-defined method of establishing naming conventions must be defined. More than likely because of my military background, I have always utilized a noun, verb, adjective approach, but it seems to work well. For example, a pump that provides service to fill a caustic tank would have a description of pump, caustic tank, filling. The motor attached to the pump would have a description of motor, pump, caustic tank filling. It may take a little getting used to, but if you define standards and utilize them throughout the system, then searching, sorting and grouping will be much easier within the system.

Equipment Tagging

011714
Pump, Caustic Tank, Filling

Figure 11: An Example of a Recommended Equipment Tag

Locations

The goal of the equipment location is to enable individuals to physically locate the equipment within the facility or site. Do not mistake this as the way to build the equipment or asset hierarchy. System dependent, there is functionality to display the equipment located in specific locations in a tree view. This functionality enhances the capabilities to define routes based on equipment or types of equipment in specific locations.

Many systems have multiple fields that may include site, building, floor, room, etc. Make use of all the location or sub-location fields as necessary to accurately identify the specific location. Establishing rails and roads may require mile markers or even yards as specific locations. Defining and standardizing locations will be critical for future development of routes and reporting information from a location perspective. For large facilities, Radio Frequency Identification (RFID) tags or a Global Positioning System (GPS) are viable options for capturing and reading latitude/longitude and locating the equipment. Locations may also contain functional locations, described as locations where specific functions occur, such as in-feed processing (refer to Figure 9).

Manufacturers

This often overlooked field or table is of extreme value if you wish to have the capabilities to determine which (by manufacturer) equipment costs more, requires more maintenance, or fails quicker (mean time to fail). Unfortunately, most organizations do not populate this field or when they do apply any standards, they are riddled with duplicate manufacturers.

Let me give you an example of what I commonly see. We'll use Allen-Bradley as the manufacturer. Imagine all the creative ways to establish it as a manufacturer:

Allen Bradley   Allen-Bradley   AlBrad   A/B   AlB   A-B   A/B AB

Take full advantage of this capability, but structure it by establishing standards and controlling who can add or modify the values. Remember spaces should be avoided.

Equipment Criticality

The goal of assigning equipment criticality is to prioritize the importance of the equipment or assets to the facility and the process. This, in conjunction with the work order priority, will assist maintenance planners in determining planning and scheduling priorities. I like to think of criticalities as the ultimate behavior driver; we respond immediately to the highest criticality ranking first. I have also learned that assignment of criticalities takes the "passion" out of the maintenance decision process and it becomes a data-driven process.

Each equipment item or asset should have a criticality code assigned. These criticalities are based on the needs and mission of the facility or process where the equipment or asset resides. They must be defined, documented, and shared across the organization. In most systems, it is merely a field entry. However, the importance of this field should not be overlooked since it will assist the organization in identifying priorities and responding appropriately.

Equipment Types/Classes

I have always considered equipment types and classes as the most powerful sort and search capabilities of a system. It allows for groupings of like-items for assignment of master tasks or procedures and searching and sorting items both vertically and horizontally within the database for detailed analysis. These fields must be defined during implementation. Not all systems allow class assignments, so it may require some creative thinking during implementation.

If you think of a typical equipment type, such as a pump, it describes what type of equipment it is. However, there could be various types of pumps within a facility. Remember one of the capabilities of this field is the assignment of master tasks (discussed in the Preventive/Predictive Maintenance and Tasks section). An equipment type of "pump" does not clearly identify the type of pump (centrifugal, positive displacement, etc.) and a search of "pump" would show all pumps. If the system you're implementing only has equipment type and no class assignment capabilities, each type of pump could be established as the following:

Equipment Type	Description
PUMP-C	Centrifugal Pump
PUMP-D	Diaphragm Pump
PUMP-P	Positive Displacement Pump
PUMP-V	Vacuum Pump

Figure 12: Equipment Type Example

If the system you're implementing has equipment class assignment capabilities, establishing "pump" would look like this:

Equipment Type	Equipment Class
PUMP	Centrifugal
	Diaphragm
	Positive Displacement
	Vacuum

Figure 13: Equipment Type and Class Assignment Example

Regardless of your system capabilities (types only or types and classes), you must define both. Most systems utilize the equipment type or class to link nameplates, specifications, or attributes data, so when you utilize a specific equipment type, the accompanying data template becomes available. Some typical items that have associated classes are motors, conveyors, instruments, etc. Ensure you develop the appropriate types and classes, but do not overdevelop and make it difficult to locate the appropriate type and class.

Operating Statuses

Some systems allow configuration of equipment operating statuses. While some are limited to a selection of "in service," it must be understood what this function actually provides. If a piece of equipment or asset is "removed from service," any repetitive tasks associated with that asset will not generate until it is returned to "in service." Operating statuses are utilized in conjunction with the "in-service" function to display the status of a piece of equipment or asset and effectively track repairable spares. A consistent set of statuses must be defined and utilized (Figure 14). By utilizing operating statuses, the status of a repairable spare can quickly be determined.

OPERATING STATUS	DESCRIPTION
ACTIVE	REPAIRABLE SPARE IN USE
REPAIR	EQUIPMENT TAKEN OUT OF SERVICE AND REPAIRED IN-HOUSE
STOCK	EQUIPMENT IS INACTIVE AND HELD IN A STORAGE LOCATION
VENDOR	EQUIPMENT TAKEN OUT OF SERVICE FOR VENDOR REPAIR

Figure 14: Operating Status Example

Nameplates/Specifications/Attributes

One of the largest data collection efforts of an implementation is the collection of nameplate information, equipment specifications, or attributes. A majority of this information is located on the equipment and must be collected in the field. Most times, the information is never established or is over-identified and contains unnecessary information. Prior to conducting this data collection effort, a few things must be established.

Identification of what will be collected is the logical starting point, yet there must be some rationale applied here to ensure only the necessary data is collected. I typically ask two questions when establishing what must be collected:

1. What must be known to identify the appropriate maintenance strategy?
2. What must be known to order a replacement?

For example, if we ask the above questions about a motor to identify a maintenance strategy: (question-1) horsepower, drive type (chain, direct drive, or belt) and lubrication requirements would be necessary. From this, it could be determined that the horsepower falls below the required level for resistance testing. It was belt driven, so a belt inspection would be required, and a motor inspection is required, and it was a lubricated motor that requires lubrication at some frequency.

To order a replacement (question-2) horsepower, RPM, frame size, enclosure, volts and amps would be required. From this information materials management or buyers could quickly identify suitable vendors for future purchasing requirements.

Templates or tables must be developed for each specific nameplate or specification that will be established within the system. These templates are normally found associated with the equipment module or area and are typically linked to equipment by the associated type and/or class. The motor identified in our above example would appear in a template as the following:

AC MOTOR NAMEPLATE/SPECIFICATION TEMPLATE	
HORSEPOWER	25
RPM	1800
DRIVE TYPE	BELT (B-52 X 3)
LUBRICATION	SHC 100 LITHIUM GREASE
FRAME SIZE	256T
ENCLOSURE	TEFC
VOLTS	230/460
AMPS	25.6/12.8

Figure 15: Nameplate/Specification Template Example

Once all templates are defined, a data collection sheet can be developed and utilized to conduct the activity in the field. This is also the best way to validate that the equipment is in service and the location is correct as well as collect the manufacturer, model, and serial number information.

Data Collection Sheet

EQUIPMENT NUMBER_____ EQUIPMENT LOCATION _____
DESCRIPTION_____
PARENT EQUIPMENT _____
MFR _____ MODEL_____ SERIAL_____
MOTOR (AC)_____
HORSEPOWER_____FRAME SIZE_____VOLTS_____AMPS_____RPM _____
ENCLOSURE_____LUBRICATION REQUIRED   YES   NO   LUBE TYPE_____
DRIVE TYPE _____ ADDITIONAL COMMENTS_____
_____
_____

Figure 16: Example of a Typical Data Collection Sheet

Parts versus Equipment

One of the most difficult discussions for the implementation team is sorting out the difference between what should be established as an asset or piece of equipment and what should be considered a part. While both are valuable, they both are established in different places within a system. Assets or equipment are established in the equipment module and become part of the hierarchy, while parts ultimately will be established within the Bill of Materials (BOM) in the materials module.

The quickest way to assist in making the part versus equipment decision is to identify what we accomplish Preventive or Predictive maintenance (PM/PdM) activities on? Those that have a defined maintenance strategy would be considered assets or equipment. What is removed and replaced upon failure? Those are typically considered parts. Use some level of caution here since, at times, there is some crossover. If you utilize the picture in Figure 17 of a conveyor, assets or equipment and parts have been identified.

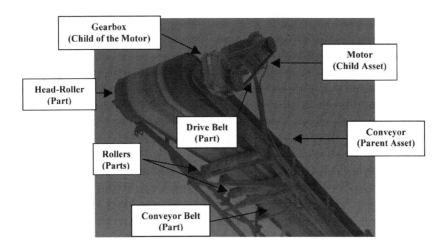

Figure 17: Parts versus Equipment Example

Meters

Most, if not all, systems have the capabilities to record metered information. Meters are typically expressed in hours or miles. The configuration and initial set up of meters varies from system to system, but fundamentally it is the identification of hours or miles and the meter range (1-XXXX- hours or miles). There are two important aspects of making the meter functionality work properly: establishing the range to determine the rollover point of the meter (i.e., 9,999.99 or 99,999.99) and collecting and entering the readings.

Meters are normally attached or read from the equipment that provides the reading. Most systems additionally will print out a meter entry sheet for collecting the readings. I normally establish a repetitive task (issued weekly) from the system to collect specific meter readings (repetitive tasks are discussed in the Job Plans and Tasks section). Meter readings are normally entered manually to each specific meter or in some interfaced circumstances directly uploaded from field data recorders. Maximum utilization of meters (where possible) should be considered to perform Preventive Maintenance (PM) based on actual usage versus a repetitive calendar frequency that may cause unnecessary or over-performance of a PM activity.

Safety Notes/Precautions

Many systems have capabilities to establish safety notes or precautions linked to equipment you have identified. Most times, this information is selected during implementation as "view only," or each time a work order is issued it could print with the work order. Keep in mind that once established with information, it must be routinely audited to ensure accuracy. I highly recommend not establishing Lock-Out-Tag-Out (LOTO) information within these data fields since most organizations manage this program in another system and do not routinely audit the information in the CMMS. To ensure you have a better chance of remembering to audit if utilizing these informational fields, establish a repetitive task (at some assigned frequency) to conduct auditing and modify the notes as necessary.

Linked or Attached Documents

Most systems have the capability to link or attach documents, drawings, web pages (if using web-enabled handheld devices) and even videos. This feature is extremely powerful to arm the maintenance workforce with all the necessary information to safely, efficiently, and effectively conduct activities without making multiple trips to review needed information. Items can be selected to print with specific Preventive Maintenance (PM) procedures or predefined tasks when the accompanying work order is printed or linked to equipment or materials for viewing. Care should be taken when utilizing this functionality to ensure you're not printing an entire operations and maintenance manual with the work order.

The key to making this functionality work is to ensure the information is stored on a server to which all users have access. This is the ideal place to attach operations and maintenance manuals, pictures, drawings, specifications, values, etc. With large numbers of maintenance talent retiring, many organizations are utilizing this functionality to video the execution of activities for future technician use in training and performing the work activity. We must seek and provide ways to make it easier for people to have the necessary information to perform activities in a proper and safe way.

Equipment History

System dependent, most equipment or assets will have a historical reference associated with each specific piece or asset established within the hierarchy. That historical reference is all completed work orders that were assigned to that equipment or asset. For this reason alone, it is imperative that equipment or assets are "tagged" to ensure accurate and appropriate history is collected and that all work is captured to a work order. Routine reviews of the historical work orders should be conducted to identify repetitive failures, mean time between failures, and refinement of the PM program. The collection of this history should be monitored to ensure an accumulation of work orders does not impact system performance. I typically recommend keeping the previous two years and the current year active and archive the remainder. Archived history in most systems can quickly be retrieved when needed.

Obviously, there are other data fields or system features associated with the equipment module or area of typical systems. These are the minimum fields and areas that must be defined, populated, and trained to the end users to ensure useable historical information is collected and meaningful equipment and maintenance decisions can be made.

Equipment Analysis

Most systems have some level of equipment data collection and analysis functionality; however, most organizations do little or nothing with it. These "codes" are called failures, problems, causes, action taken, or remedies in most systems.

A note of caution about these codes: maintenance or reliability engineers feel the failure code is actually the failure mode, so grouping them by equipment type eliminates the utilization of some generic codes. They also feel these "codes," to be successful, must rely on the maintenance technician to identify the specific failure (or mode), i.e. "the bearing seized" and the remedy "replaced the bearing." The determination of the cause is best left to a maintenance or reliability engineering function. Numerous factors must be investigated to determine what caused the bearing to fail (improper installation, improper lubrication, misalignment, overloading, brinneling, etc.). Without failure analysis, time, and education, an average maintenance technician will not know the true root causes of the failure.

Once established within the system, these "codes" collect what failed, what caused the failure, and what action was required to fix the failure. Some systems bundle these together and present them as a troubleshooting tree or potential solutions and tie them back to specific equipment types (i.e., centrifugal pumps, etc.). Keep this in mind when establishing your equipment types and classes to ensure you can take advantage of this functionality. Some systems display this information in a logic tree view (see Figure 18) by equipment type based on work order entries, completions, and the utilization of the appropriate codes by the organization.

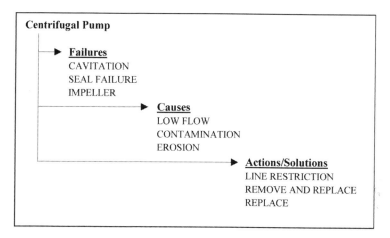

Figure 18: Failure, Cause, Actions, or Solutions Logic Tree Example

As we complete the current transition of retiring maintenance resources and establishing their replacements, this information can be invaluable to an organization since it is based on historical events of your equipment at your site.

When developing these tables, again, think of the end user and do not overdevelop and make it difficult to provide the correct information. The intent of this information is to understand failures and their causes, not point fingers, otherwise you'll collect misinformation.

Failures or Problems

Figure 19 defines typical failures throughout a site or facility. This is an example only; you must define your failures based on the equipment at your site.

FAILURE	FAILURE DESCRIPTION
Bad Connection	Unable to make connection.
Breaker Trips	Circuit breaker trips when utilizing equipment.
Can't Start	Equipment will not start.
Jammed	Product jammed, unable to operate.
Product Leak	Product leaks while operating.
Out of Adjustment	Unable to adjust to operate at rated flow, speed, etc.
Instrument Failure	Instrument (speed, pressure, temperature, etc.) not functioning.
Failure to stop	Equipment does not stop when shut down.
Erratic Operation	Equipment operates erratically when in use.

Figure 19: Failure Example

Causes

Figure 20 defines typical causes of failures throughout a site or facility. This is an example only; you must define your causes.

CAUSE	CAUSE DESCRIPTION
Improper Operation	Induced by improper equipment operation.
Improper Maintenance	Induced by improper maintenance activity.
Design Defect	Induced by an engineering design defect.
Parts Defect	Induced by a parts defect or failure. Typically this occurs shortly after a new part is installed. Ensure it is a parts defect and not an improper maintenance defect.
Lubrication	Induced by lack of, improper, or over lubrication.
Unbalance	Induced by excessive vibration due to equipment not being properly balanced.
Alignment	Induced by severe misalignment.
Worn (Beyond Life)	Induced by equipment, component, or part being worn beyond its useful life.
Improper Usage	Induced by improper equipment or component usage that exceeds operational parameters (i.e., ratings exceeded) or equipment utilized for unintended purposes.

Figure 20: Cause Example

Action Taken or Remedies

Figure 21 defines typical actions taken or solutions throughout a site or facility to address work accomplished on a work order. This is an example only; you must define your actions.

ACTION TAKEN	ACTION TAKEN DESCRIPTION
Replaced	Item, material, or part was replaced with like item from the materials management function. These items could be certified rebuilt items issued from the storeroom.
Repaired	Item, material, or part was repaired but not replaced with a new or rebuilt item.
Temporary Repair	A temporary repair was performed due to parts, materials, or labor availability. This action taken will inform the maintenance planner that a new work order must be established, planned, and scheduled for future permanent repair.
Cleaned	The removal of debris and foreign matter (i.e., product, dust, dirt, grease, etc.) that has or may have an impact on the reliable operation of equipment or environmental related.
Adjusted	An adjustment was made to ensure the equipment was/is operating at normal operating conditions. These adjustments could be speed, pressure, flow, temperature, or other adjustments.
Inspected	The visual inspection in the performance of a PM activity. This action taken is only utilized and associated with the PM work order type.
Deferred	The deferment (non-performance) of a PM activity that has been scheduled but not performed due to equipment or labor availability.
Lubricated	The application of lubrication, typically this activity is performed by the lubrication technicians.

Figure 21: Action Taken or Solution Example

Materials Management

The materials management module or area is very similar to the equipment module or area and has the same requirements for defining inventory numbers, types, descriptions, etc. All too often, this module never becomes fully populated. To maximize the utilization of planning and scheduling of maintenance activities, this module is a must.

The quick identification of necessary parts or materials, their locations, and the quantities on hand are critical to the efficient execution of maintenance activities. In the equipment section we discussed the importance of establishing each asset or piece of equipment. The same rational applies here, and we must establish the items used in support of maintaining that equipment.

Each item in inventory should have a "where used" identified, a location of where that item is in the storeroom, and most important, established min/max levels or reorder points so needed items are always available. One of the fastest ways to improve maintenance productivity is to not allow maintenance resources to wander up and down storeroom aisles looking for needed parts. They must be trained to utilize the system to quickly locate the required part(s) and their physical location to accomplish maintenance activities effectively and efficiently.

Most organizations complain that there is no management of materials. The CMMS is the ideal collection point for all materials management information. Again, this will require that culture of discipline to ensure all parts and materials are established within the system and that they are captured on the work order when issued. To fully enable this to provide meaningful information, a few things must be established. All parts must reside within the system with accurate descriptions, valid prices must be assigned, and the physical location and quantity must be populated. Additionally, to fully reap the benefits of utilizing the CMMS as a materials management tool, fundamental elements must be established, such as inventory types and classes, primary and alternate vendors, primary and alternate vendors, primary and alternate part numbers, metrics or Key Performance Indicators (KPIs), and Bill of Materials (BOM) information.

Inventory Types and Classes

These are utilized to group and categorize items, much like the equipment type and class previously discussed in the equipment section. If properly identified, inventory types and classes (Figure 22) facilitate quick searching for items. Typical types may be as broad as "bearing" and have an assigned class of "roller." Not all systems allow users to establish classes. With these systems (type only), meaningful types must be developed to enable quick searching and sorting of the inventory. Because of character limitations in some systems, you may have to get creative in identifying types. In doing so, be sure the description clearly identifies what the type is (Figure 23) and that it is documented in the Standard Operating Procedures document.

Inventory Type	Inventory Class
BELT	Conveyor
	Timing
	Drive
BEARING	Ball
	Flange
	Needle
	Pillow Block
CYLINDER	Air
	Hydraulic

Figure 22: Inventory Type and Class Assignment Example

Inventory Type	Description
BELT-C	Belt, Conveyor
BELT-T	Belt, Timing
BELT-V	Belt, Drive V
BEARING-B	Bearing, Ball
BEARING-F	Bearing, Flange
BEARING-N	Bearing, Needle
BEARING-PB	Bearing, Pillow Block
CYL-A	Cylinder, Air
CYL-H	Cylinder, Hydraulic

Figure 23: Inventory Type Example

Unit of Measure, Purchase, and Issue

In most systems, unit of measure (UOM), purchase (UOP) and issue (UOI) is a shared table (all the values are established within one table but utilized in multiple fields or areas). The table in Figure 24 defines how items and services are purchased, measured, and issued. This information must be defined at implementation. For example, safety glasses that are a stocked item in the storeroom might be purchased by the case but are issued by the pair. Or in services, a contractor to perform activities may be purchased by the month, but measured by the hour (160 hours). Care must be utilized in the assignment of these values, specifically with inventory records and establishing the unit of issue. I have seen numerous organizations purchase by the case (50 items) and issue individually, so every issue would trigger a reorder since the system assumed you issued by the case (50 items).

Unit of Measure, Purchase and Issue	Description
BOX	Purchased or issued by the box
CASE	Purchased or issued by the case
HOUR	Purchased and measured by the hour
FOOT	Purchased or issued by the foot
CY	Purchased by the cubic yard
GALLON	Purchased or issued by the gallon
50BX	Purchased by the box of 50

Figure 24: Unit of Measure, Purchase, and Issue Example

Primary and Alternate Vendors

This data is typically established during implementation of the purchasing portion of the system and is utilized in materials management or inventory as well. Ensure the primary and alternate vendor (if applicable) for each item is identified. Having this information readily available (especially if you have taken the time to identify lead times) is critical for an accurate mean time to accomplish activities while factoring in lead times for items.

Much like the discussion in the employee's section of this book, numbers or names can be utilized. I have always tried to utilize names whenever possible; it is much easier to equate the name of the vendor ABC Company than it is 11735 = ABC Company. Additionally, some systems utilize "branches" to further identify companies and specific vendors by location. For example ABC Company could be established as a vendor and a branch of Kansas City could be established to identify that vendor and its specific vendor location or store.

Warehouses, Storerooms, and Stock Locations

Warehouses or storerooms must be defined and established during the implementation of the system. These are defined as the physical buildings or locations where the parts or materials will be contained. Once the "building" is established, the physical location of the part or material within the building or location must be defined. This is typically accomplished by establishing row, shelf, and bin information. What row or aisle within the warehouse will it be stored on, what shelf will it be placed upon, and if stored in a bin, what bin is it contained in? This information is populated for each material item number, a quantity is established, and a cost assigned.

Additionally, it may be helpful to establish a "virtual" warehouse for parts kits and their storage. A virtual warehouse could be a reserved area within an established area where parts kits could be stored and managed. This would help keep them visible and assist in protecting them from routine issue.

Inventory Costing Methods

An initial costing method must be set up for the warehouse or storeroom to define the organization's inventory costing method. System dependent, each established warehouse or storeroom could have a different costing method while some systems only allow one type for all established. One of the following methods must be utilized, shown in Figure 25.

Inventory Costing Method	Description
Last In First Out (LIFO)	LIFO assumes that the last item entered is used first and the costing of that last purchase is the costing for all like items in stock. There could be tax advantages or disadvantages associated with LIFO.
First In First Out (FIFO)	FIFO assumes that the first item entered is the first item used. Using this method provides nearly current costing information.
Weighted Average	Weighted average is the calculation of the cost of the current inventory, plus the cost of the new purchase, divided by the quantity on hand.

Figure 25: Inventory Costing Method

Reorder Methods

Systems typically utilize min/max or Reorder Points (ROP) to establish the organization's reorder method. Utilizing min/max, a minimum quantity is established for each item and a maximum quantity on hand is established. When the minimum quantity is reached, a notification (or an automatic reorder) is generated to replenish stock back to the maximum level.

Utilizing the Reorder Point (ROP) requires more initial work upfront but provides greater accuracy. Reorder points are normally calculated by understanding the demand for an item, the lead time to receive the item, the safety point for the item, and forecasting the future item usage. This is where the planning effort can pay huge dividends by identifying, reserving, and developing parts kits to assist in the forecasting.

Reserving Parts

Most systems allow some type of parts reservations. Parts reservations are typically executed by the maintenance planner during the planning of maintenance activities. Items required are identified and annotated with the quantity required through a parts picking function within the system. The warehouse or the storeroom receives this "reservation" notification from the system indicating the item, the quantity required, the item's location, and the work order number associated with the activity. This is known as a "soft reservation" in many systems; until physically issued, it is considered on the shelf. At times this can get confusing if there is only one available (which has a reservation) but is still considered "on the shelf" by the system.

Parts Kitting

Parts kitting works in conjunction with the parts reservation function. Parts are identified by the planner, a pick list is developed, and the warehouse or storeroom fulfills the requirements of the list. If all items are available, they are pulled from stock and placed in a bag, box, or pallet and annotated with the work order number. The planner is notified, and the work is scheduled. This is a very simple explanation of a complex process, and I encourage you to read *"Kitting in Maintenance Made Simple"* by Daniel DeWald and Jeff Shiver to successfully implement the process.

Bill of Materials (BOM)

The identification of required materials, quantities, manufacturers, vendors, full descriptions, lead times, and unit costs are all items necessary to identify an accurate Bill of Materials (BOM). These are normally linked to or are associated with each piece of equipment. Once fully developed, it allows maintenance resources to quickly identify needed materials from a listing of items attached to the equipment number while avoiding searching the entire inventory database. This allows them to find the necessary items without roaming the warehouse or storeroom. Some systems display this information within the equipment hierarchy below each piece of equipment or asset while others display it as a listing. Regardless of how the system displays it, this is critical maintenance information that enables maintenance personnel to become more effective and efficient.

Obviously, the best time to collect BOM information is at the purchase of the equipment. If not, this data must be collected and populated. The best way to ensure it gets started is every item (not to include consumable items) must have a minimum of one instance of "where used." Identify which piece of equipment or asset utilizes that part. This will ultimately assist in the identification of obsolete items within the warehouse or storeroom. If an asset is removed from service, and there is no other "where used" identified for it, then it could be considered obsolete and removed.

Additionally, some systems build BOM information "on the fly." As items are issued to equipment or assets if they are not contained on the existing BOM, they can be added. Care must be used if utilizing this functionality and review each entry prior to accepting it or consumable or incorrect items could be added to the BOM.

Linked or Attached Documents

As discussed in the equipment section of this book, the capability to link or attach documents, drawings, etc., is typically available in the inventory module or area of most systems. Attaching vendor drawings or specifications for inventory items is valuable. I also find it helpful if a picture of the item is attached so potential users can view the item without removing it from the shelf and tearing the protective box or wrapper from the item.

Inventory Transactions

Inventory transactions are recorded in the system for each action against an item. Issues, returns, receipts, price changes, orders, physical or cycle counts transactions are kept as part of the item history. This item history, much like the equipment history, should be routinely reviewed to fully understand inventory items.

Purchasing

The purchasing module or area tracks requests for purchases of parts, materials, services, receipt of those purchases and invoices for purchases. Obtaining the materials and services required to complete work is an important part of any maintenance process. As inventory balances decrease in the storerooms, you must replenish those balances. Most systems offer some level of purchasing capabilities. Along with these purchasing capabilities, most systems also include a request for quotations, purchase requisitioning, receiving, invoicing, and vendor analysis.

Although nearly all these features are available within most systems, many organizations do not utilize the purchasing functionality. Most organizations use purchasing software applications separately from their CMMS, and many times it is never interfaced with the CMMS. If not interfaced, duplicate entries must occur in the purchasing system and the maintenance management system; otherwise, the CMMS contains no costing information for parts, materials, or services. Additionally, if parts are purchased through an external non-interfaced system, the receiving of parts in the CMMS is a manual entry process that must be defined. Regardless, it is critical that the inventory stock levels contained within the CMMS are kept accurate.

If you look holistically at what a CMMS provides, the most critical aspect is the cost of parts/materials and labor costs. By not entering the cost of parts, materials, or services, fifty percent of the costing information normally available is discarded.

The Purchase Order (PO) application is used to create and manage purchase orders for items, materials, services, tools, etc. Depending on your defined business processes, POs may automatically be created from Purchase Requisitions (PRs), or a buyer may need to review and approve the PR before creating a PO. Large dollar purchases may require the creation of a Request for Quotation (RFQ). The RFQ is used to request from vendors their bids for needed items. Once quotations have been awarded, you can create purchase contracts and POs from an RFQ.

Purchase Requisitions

A Purchase Requisition (PR) is a written request issued internally to order items or services. When maintenance work requires parts, materials, or services that cannot be supplied from internal warehouses, storerooms, or labor pool, a PR is created. The purchasing department uses the purchase requisition to create either a Request for Quotation for the items or services, or a Purchase Order after the purchase is approved.

Requests for Quotations

A Request for Quotation (RFQ) is a request that is sent to one or multiple potential vendors. In these requests, specific costing and conditions for the delivery of an item or service can be identified. In the RFQ record, you can specify line items, required delivery dates, and other conditions you want the vendor to meet for the delivery of the item or service.

Request for Proposals

A Request for Proposal (RFP) is similar to an RFQ but is generally used for a large number of items or services. Circumstances might require you to obtain quotations from several vendors before deciding from which one to purchase materials or services. With the RFP, you can review store quotations received from vendors, analyze quotations in order to make purchasing decisions, and use the information to create Purchase Orders.

Purchase Order Type	Description
Standard	Typically the normal default for Purchase Orders created.
Change	A change order is a duplicate purchase order generated from an approved purchase order. If you must change an approved PO that has no receipts, you can create a change order. The change order preserves the audit trail by retaining the original PO while making necessary changes to the change order PO.
Release	Used to indicate a release type PO when a blanket purchase order has been generated.
Service	Used to indicate the purchase order is for services.

Figure 26: Purchase Order Types

Purchasing and Inventory

The purchasing module works closely with the inventory module to maintain balances of items and materials in system-established storerooms or warehouses. When items are reordered, the system creates one or more purchasing record(s) for the reorder. When purchase requests are received, one of several types of records can be created: unapproved or approved purchase requisitions, or unapproved or approved purchase orders (dependent on the established reorder method and business process). Internal and external purchase requisitions and orders can be defined that establish centralized purchasing. If in the event of multiple storerooms or warehouses, one could be identified as the "main" and all "satellite" storerooms could use internal purchase requisitions or orders to replenish their stock from the "main" storeroom or warehouse. External requisitions or orders would be utilized for the "main" to replenish stock for all external parts, material, or services from vendors.

Purchase Requisition and Order Line Types

Purchase requisitions and orders list each item or service to be purchased on an individual line. Each purchase requisition or purchase order line should have a line item type specified for it. Figure 27 illustrates typical line item types.

PR and PO Line Types	Description
Item	Used to order inventory items that have material item records created for them.
Material	Used to order items or materials on a one-time basis, that is items that do not have item records created for them in the inventory.
Service	Used to order services on a one-time basis.
Standard	Used to order services that are regularly ordered.
Tools	Used to order tools that are created for tracking purposes.
Special Order	Used to order rare or unusual items or materials not typically ordered.

Figure 27: Purchasing Line Type Examples

Invoices and Invoice Types

An invoice is a bill from a vendor for delivered products or services. The invoice can record notes from vendors and match invoice details against Purchase Orders and receipts. Invoicing lets you match invoice information against Purchase Order and receipts of materials and services, so the invoice can be approved and ultimately paid. Some typical invoice types are invoice (the default) used to indicate a payment to a vendor, credit to indicate a credit was issued to a vendor, or debit used to indicate an additional charge not listed on an invoice.

Receipts

A receipt is a record of goods or services received from a vendor. The receipt function is to receive materials into inventory. You can use the receipts functionality to receive materials that have arrived as ordered, record partial shipments, and record items returned to vendors. For example, items that have failed an inspection and have been rejected would be recorded as items returned to vendors. Additionally, receipts for services can be defined to record services received against an approved Purchase Order.

Receiving Materials

Information about items received must come from an approved Purchase Order (PO). You can copy all the PO line items to the material receipts if the entire order has been received, or you can enter partial receipts. For example, if items are back ordered or parts of a large shipment arrive separately, you can record these as partial receipts. You also can record receipt of the materials ordered on the PO and note any discrepancies between what was ordered, received, and rejected. You also can receive materials not tracked in inventory but requiring a PO. For example, you might order a new desk, which would not be stored in inventory or tracked by a material item number. You would, however, want to track them on Purchase Orders and receipts.

Receiving Services

Service receipts refer to data associated with any service provided by a vendor or contractor. The service can be performed on or off site. You specify service purchases either in terms of a quantity and a unit cost or as a single lump sum amount. Whichever term you use on the service Purchase Order, they must be the same on the corresponding receipt transaction. You can copy all Purchase Order line items to the Service Receipts if all services have been received, or you can enter partial receipts. When utilizing service receipts, two things happen:

1. Receipts of services are recorded after a contractor or vendor submits a claim.
2. An authorized individual must validate the costs of services and approve the receipt. Services always require approval.

Employees or Labor

The employee or labor module area should contain all resources within the organization that will utilize the system or perform work order activity. Most systems require each system user to be established as an employee, assigned to a security role or profile, and have a craft associated with that employee.

Identifying Crafts

Identification of crafts is similar to the roles that were identified within the system security configuration (management, supervisors, maintenance planner, operations or production, buyers, materials management, human resources, etc.). The exception is crafts associated with maintenance must be further defined to support appropriate craft assignment to work orders. It may be necessary to develop a matrix (Figure 28) if the organization contains multiple crafts across the organization.

Security Role	Craft
MANAGEMENT	MANAGER
SUPERVISOR (MAINTENANCE)	SUPERVISOR
MAINTENANCE PLANNER	PLANNER
SUPERVISOR (PRODUCTION)	SUPERVISOR
MAINTENANCE CRAFTS	MECHANICIAL ELECTRICAL INSTRUMENTATION MILLWRIGHT WELDER PIPEFITTER
PRODUCTION	PRODUCTION
BUYERS	BUYER
MATERIALS MANAGEMENT	MATERIALS MANAGEMENT
HUMAN RESOURCES	HR
RELIABILITY ENGINEERING	RELIABILITY ENGINEER

Figure 28: Craft to Role Assignment Example

The proper identification of maintenance crafts is critical to support the planning and scheduling functions, facilitate assignment of the appropriate craft to work orders, and establish accurate maintenance backlog information. If contract labor is utilized, a "contractor" craft should be established to facilitate assignment of work orders to contractors for scheduling and coordination.

Once all crafts are identified, each craft must have an hourly burdened labor (with benefits and fringe) rate assigned to capture accurate labor costing information. Unfortunately, many organizations utilize an across the organization average (often extremely low) or have no labor rates assigned at all. If you look at what a typical system provides, labor cost to perform activities, material costs associated with those activities, foundational elements for lifecycle cost analysis, and the capability to provide real-time maintenance budgeting information, why would you not populate accurate costing information?

If there is concern about labor rates being visible to employees, remember fields or tables associated with rates can be hidden from all users and not displayed, except to the system administrator. Keep in mind these rates change and as rates change, the system must change to reflect the most current rate.

Employee Schedules and Availability

When employees are established, most systems require the assignment of availability or schedules. While this is not necessary for all employees, it is critical for any employee that will be assigned activities through work orders, specifically maintenance personnel.

When defining schedules, you need to consider "true availability." Although a typical schedule may be eight hours, not all is considered schedulable time, so lunch and breaks should be deducted. Normally, schedules are entered for daily availability for a typical work week for each employee. While some systems have the capability to establish rotating shifts, some do not. Additionally, many systems require the site or facility schedule to be established to identify the normal days of operation. It is important if the system your organization utilizes requires site schedules to populate this scheduling data to support the generation of repetitive tasks, so they only generate on normal work days.

Generally associated with the scheduling aspects of sites or facilities and employees are scheduling exceptions. These exceptions are to identify reasons the site or an employee is not available or, in some cases, has increased availability (overtime). Some systems refer to this as the "factory calendar" where entry of the non-working days for the site is established (i.e. company holidays). This is normally a shared table for the site and the employee and must be defined during implementation. Figure 29 offers examples of scheduling exceptions.

SCHEDULING EXCEPTION	DESCRIPTION
JURY DUTY	JURY DUTY
FLA	FAMILY LEAVE ACT
HOLIDAY	COMPANY HOLIDAY
RESERVE	MILITARY RESERVE DUTY
SICK	SICK LEAVE
TRAINING	IN-HOUSE OR ON-SITE TRAINING
VACATION	VACATION
OVERTIME	OVERTIME

Figure 29: Scheduling Exception Example

To fully utilize the work order scheduling functionality of most systems, the schedules must be populated and kept current. When individuals are assigned known overtime, the exception overtime and the additional hours are entered, the available hours for the individual and the "pool" of available hours increases. When an individual is on vacation and the days are entered and the scheduling exception vacation is utilized, the available hours for the individual and the "pool" are reduced. By utilizing this functionality, the real maintenance availability stays accurate.

When defining employees, consider all system users; some systems call them employee codes, and it is assumed by many a code or number must be utilized when establishing individuals. An employee number is utilized by many organizations. System dependent, this could make it difficult to assign individuals to work orders without creating additional look-up sheets to correlate employee codes to employees. Try to utilize names, starting with the last name then first name (SMITH-BOB, for example). Some names, because of system induced field limits, may not fit entirely.

There are numerous fields for data population within typical employee or labor records; however, many are not necessary since they duplicate information kept in Human Resources (HR) management systems and are not needed for proper system utilization. The key fields to populate are the employee, craft, assigned department, shift, and the associated burdened labor rate.

Work Orders

The work order module or area is where the various work types and/ or work classes reside. This is the heartbeat of the system and enables the collection of history, the identification of the maintenance backlog, and provides Key Performance Indicators (KPI) or metrics for maintenance management. These are the system enablers; once a work order is created, it establishes a transactional record that resides within the system (forever).

This is the functionality that allows the system to be utilized as a communication tool while providing data for reporting and data harvesting opportunities. To ensure collection of valuable historical information, a culture of disciple must be established to ensure all maintenance and equipment-related activities are captured within the work order system. Remember, there is no such thing as an insignificant maintenance or equipment event, so all should be captured.

Look at the different work types and see if all the typical work your maintenance resources accomplish is quickly identifiable. If you don't see it as a work order type, you won't see it in any reports. Work order priorities are typically defined here to help planners understand how quickly the work requested must be planned and scheduled.

Work Requests or Service Requests

Most systems have work or service requests that ultimately become work orders once they are approved. They provide documentation and identification of the work that needs to be performed and typically are relatively simple to enter. Work or service requests are not authorizations to proceed with work or issue materials for repairs, they are only a request.

Emergency Work Orders

Some systems have unique work orders that are specific for emergency response. These work orders require minimum information (equipment or asset number and a description of the issue) to facilitate quick entry and normally require no approval. Material issues and labor charges may be immediately posted to these types of work orders.

Work Order Types

Work order types (Figure 30) allow for a grouping of the type of work performed (i.e., emergency, preventive, safety, etc.). Ensure these groupings fit the actual types of work performed by the personnel at your site or facility. Detailed work order types allow for segregation and sorting of work performed and allow organizations to see where and how resources are utilized. Detailed documentation of each work type and when to utilize them should be developed and disseminated to each system user to ensure standardized usage for data harvesting opportunities. Additionally, it must be understood that in the identification of the types of work performed by maintenance resources, non-maintenance work is a large part of the activities as well.

WORK ORDER TYPE	DESCRIPTION
CALIBRATION	Used to indicate work associated with the calibration program.
CORRECTIVE	Used for any repair work that is identified during the performance of a Preventive or Predictive Maintenance (PM or PdM) task. When these repairs are identified, they should be documented in the comments section of the PM or PdM work order, and a new work order of this type is written. This work order type is utilized for PM or PdM program justification.
EMERGENCY	Used to track unplanned run to failure type work or reactive breakdowns.
PdM	Used for predictive maintenance tasks, including vibration analysis, infrared analysis, oil analysis, and ultrasonic analysis.
PM	Used for any scheduled repetitive task based on frequency intervals or meter readings, including lubrications, cleanings and inspections.
PROJECT	Used for work associated with long-term or capital projects or installations.
REBUILD	Used to record the costs associated with the overhaul or major rebuild of equipment.
SAFETY	Used for all safety inspections and maintenance or repairs on safety equipment and/or systems.
PLANNED	Used for any work identified during the course of the normal workday.
SHUTDOWN	Used to group all work to be accomplished during a scheduled outage or shutdown.
TRAINING	Used to document man-hours expended for reportable training.

Figure 30: Work Order Types Example

Work Order Classes

Work order classes allow further definition and grouping of the type of work being performed. Utilizing Figure 31, the cost and hours of performing Predictive Maintenance (PdM) activities would be available by the work order type (total costing), and the class would allow a drilldown understanding of each of the individual program costs and hours expended.

WORK ORDER TYPE	WORK ORDER CLASS
PdM	Vibration Analysis
	Oil Analysis
	Infrared Thermography
	Ultrasonic Testing
	Non-Destructive Testing
PROJECT	Production
	Environmental
	Safety
	Facilities

Figure 31: Work Order Type and Class Assignment Example

Work Order Priorities

Work order priorities are value assignments that identify how important the required work is and dictate the mean time to response. These priorities are often abused by organizations, and as such, they should be utilized to identify mean time to plan and mean time to accomplish. Again, to ensure that priorities do not lose the intended meaning, they should be documented and disseminated to each user and routinely monitored to ensure utilization conforms to the identified standards.

Work order priorities in many circumstances are merely assigned from a pull-down menu containing numbers (1-10, A - E, etc.). These priorities must be defined during implementation (see Figure 32). Training on planning and scheduling of maintenance activities could be extremely helpful in determining the appropriate priorities for your organization.

Priority		Priority Description
1	Emergency	Unplanned emergency work: immediate response necessary. **Overtime authorized**. Current week focus.
2	Urgent	Unplanned work: cannot wait for formal planning. **Overtime not authorized**. Current week focus.
3	PM's	Planned condition and time based Preventive Maintenance (PM) work. Should be less than 20-30% of the planned work.
4	Essential Planned	Highest priority of planned work after PM's. Should consume 60% of the remaining planned hours.
5	Highly Desirable Planned	Medium priority of planned work. Should consume 25% of the remaining planned hours.
6	Least Consequence Planned	Lowest priority of planned work. Should consume 15% of the planned remaining hours. Ideal for reactive troubleshooting, shift coverage, etc.

Figure 32: Work Order Priority Example

Work Order Statuses

Many think these statuses automate their process, and it just happens from that point on. Unfortunately, the statuses that drive a work order through its life cycle (creation to closure) are not automatic and require manual intervention.

When manual intervention is required, how confident are you that the people who must provide that intervention understand or even know they are part of the process? Many don't know, and it is evident when you hear people say, "Did you see that work order that I put in?" or "When will my work get completed?" Your system should be considered a communication tool which utilizes work orders to communicate and statuses to amplify that communication.

Although it is something typically done at implementation, many never define what's required, who must do it, and what action is required. When you look at the organizations that struggle with this, the underlying issue is a lack of defined work management flows and processes. To accurately define the statuses necessary for inclusion, it must be done utilizing the work flow and processes that were defined for the organization. I have found it helpful to develop it in a chart format (Figure 33) that defines the work order status, the required system action, the involved role(s), the required role action, and the next acceptable status. If this is developed, it becomes very transparent to the organization.

Work Order Status	Required System Action	Involved Role(s)	Required Action	Next Status
Open	New order/request entered into system	Originator	Automatic system assignment	Pending Approval
Pending Approval	Resides in the system indicating orders/requests awaiting approval	Supervisor	Approve or disapprove order/request	Awaiting Planning Ready Cancel
Awaiting Planning	Resides in the system indicating work orders that are awaiting planning	Supervisor Planner	Select next status	In Planning
In Planning	Resides in the system indicating work orders that are in the planning process	Planner	Select next status	Ready Awaiting Parts
Awaiting Parts	Resides in the system indicating necessary parts are not available to complete the activity. The work order remains in this status until all required parts to complete the activity are received	Planner Storeroom	Select next status	Ready
Ready	Resides in the system indicating work order is ready for scheduling and execution	Supervisor Planner	Select next status	Scheduled
Scheduled	Resides in the system indicating the work order is scheduled for completion	Supervisor Planner	Select next status	Complete Reschedule In-Work
In-Work	Resides in the system indicating work orders that are currently in work	Supervisor Maintenance	Select next status	Complete Reschedule
Complete	Resides in the system indicating work orders that are completed and ready for planning review	Supervisor Maintenance	Select next status	Closed
Reschedule	Resides in the system indicating work orders that must be rescheduled for completion	Supervisor Planner	Select next status	Ready
Closed	Resides in the system indicating work orders that have been completed and reviewed by planning	Planner	Work order is committed to history no further action required	
Cancel	Resides in the system indicating work orders that were canceled or not approved	Supervisor Planner	Select next status	Closed

Figure 33: Work Order Status and Required Actions Example

61

Depending on the system you utilize, there are only a few potential "automated" status opportunities, such as placing a demand for a part and the part is not available. Some systems automatically assign Awaiting Parts, or upon entry of a new work order/request, Pending Approval is automatically assigned.

So as you can see, there is a significant amount of manual intervention required, but by developing a chart and training the organization, communication happens as a result of utilizing work orders. There could be additional statuses that you may have to define, but if you follow this same methodology, you'll be successful.

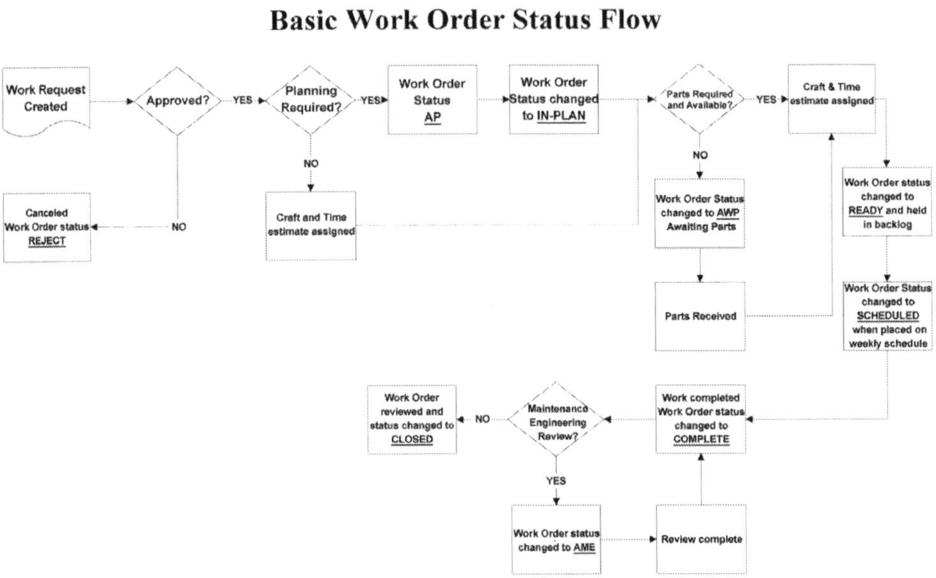

Basic Work Order Status Flow

Figure 34: Basic Work Order Status Flow Example

The work order, its utilization, and the standardized flow are some of the most crucial elements of your system for work management. This is the data trigger point that enables the collection of all data for review and analysis. Significant time and energy should be spent to ensure it is established correctly, utilized properly, and then monitored for ongoing conformity.

Take extra care to establish a culture of discipline to ensure all maintenance work performed in your organization is through the work order system. Audit periodically by comparing payroll hours to work order hours captured within your system. Remember, if it didn't get into a work order, it never happened.

Work Order Auditing

The purpose of the work order audit is to validate existing processes while identifying improvement opportunities, understand the mean-time between statuses, and ensure appropriate historical information is collected. Several elements must be reviewed following a work order through its lifecycle (creation to closure). Start with the work request entry and follow it through approval, planning, scheduling, execution, and close out.

The work order selected for the audit must have been processed through the normal work management process. Ideally, a work order with known issues is utilized to identify process or system deficiencies. Remember the goal is the identification of issues not individuals with issues.

I have always viewed this opportunity as a validation and learning experience. An audit team should be utilized with interviews of all who were part of the activity and reviews of the data submitted focusing on the identification of work management process issues or data gaps. Follow the established work management process (Figure 35):

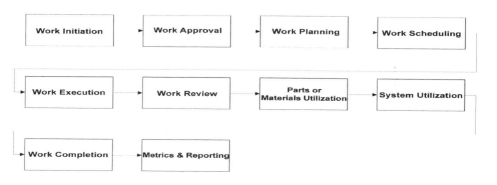

Figure 35: Work Order Audit Process Flow Example

At a minimum this audit should be performed monthly to validate processes and ensure data standards provide the necessary information.

Job Plans or Tasks

The job plans or task area or module is where the detailed descriptions and step-by-step guides for maintenance activities reside. These job plans or tasks should specify the appropriate craft(s), any tools, materials, job steps, associated safety notes or precautions, and estimated times to complete the job. Each system establishes these procedures a little differently, but the output is fundamentally the same; a work order with details of what, how and with whom to accomplish the activity is identified. These procedures are not limited to Preventive or Predictive Maintenance (PM or PdM) procedures and may be developed for any task that is routinely performed.

A job plan or task is a template containing a detailed description of work to be performed on an asset or a location. Job plans or tasks should be reusable, meaning each time the activity is performed, that plan or task can be reused. A job plan or task may be applied to an unlimited number of work orders. A job plan or task typically includes procedural descriptions, estimated labor, parts or materials, services, and tools to be used on the job.

Defining Job Plans or Tasks

Job plans or tasks are the library of reusable procedures contained within the system. This is where system differences exist on how the plans or tasks are developed. While some systems require each step to be identified, others utilize a more holistic approach and allow you to write instructions or tasks. However, both types of systems allow you to link or combine multiple plans or tasks together and issue them as one work order. For example, a conveyor has a task that requires an inspection. It has an attached motor and gearbox, and you want to inspect them all at the same time. Since each piece of equipment or asset would have a job plan(s) or task(s) defined, you could issue individual tasks or link them together and issue as one task on one work order.

Utilizing the step approach (Figure 36), details are defined within steps or instructions to be accomplished. Each step may have a unique craft, materials, and estimated time to accomplish the step.

Step	Conveyor Details or Procedure
10	Inspect the conveyor frame for rust or corrosion.
20	Inspect the head roller for.....
30	Inspect the tail roller for....

Step	AC Motor Details or Procedure
10	Inspect the foundation mounting for...
20	Inspect the air intake for.....
30	Inspect the tail roller for....

Step	Gearbox Details or Procedure
10	Inspect the mounting for...
20	Inspect the oil level sight glass for...
30	Inspect for leaks....

Figure 36: Linking or Combining Job Plans or Tasks

These three job plans or tasks could be linked or combined into one work order containing all steps with a total estimated time to accomplish the activity.

Utilizing the holistic approach (Figure 37), each piece of equipment or asset would have a defined task.

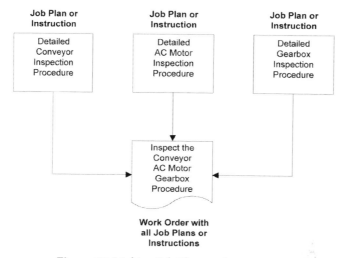

Figure 37: Linking Job Plans or Instructions

Nested or Shadowed Tasks

Most systems utilize a functionality called shadowing or nesting of repetitive tasks based on the assigned frequency. There may be tasks defined that are a monthly inspection followed by a quarterly service. To minimize the "out-of-service" time, shadowing or nesting will combine the activities of the monthly and the quarterly every third month. This feature is typically utilized in inspecting and servicing fleets; however, there are other applications for this in routine Preventive Maintenance (PM) and they should be explored.

Frequency Assignments

Frequency assignments (Figure 38) must be defined for system generation of repetitive tasks. Although the identification of frequencies seems relatively straightforward, it is not. Documenting the frequencies within the Standard Operating Procedure (SOP) is necessary. Some systems have calendar (weekly, monthly, etc.) and daily (Monday, Tuesday, etc.) frequencies established within them. The daily frequencies are useful for establishing activities that you wish to complete on specific days. For example, every Tuesday a visual inspection could be scheduled, or it could be established as every other Tuesday by entering the "2" prefix (2-Tuesday).

Frequency	Description	Frequency Conversion
Day(s)	Utilized for any task with a scheduling period of 1-6 day(s). The prefix or perform every $\underline{X}$ days would indicate the frequency (i.e. 3-Days would issue every 3 days).	
Week(s)	Utilized for any task with a scheduling period of 1-4 week(s). The prefix or perform every $\underline{X}$ weeks would indicate the frequency (i.e. 2-Weeks would issue every 2 weeks).	Biweekly frequency will be established as every 2 week(s).
Month(s)	Utilized for any task with a scheduling period of 1-12 month(s) or more. The prefix or perform every $\underline{X}$ month would indicate the frequency (i.e. 3-Months would issue every 3 months).	Quarterly frequency will be established as every 3 month(s) Semiannual will be established as every 6 month(s)
Year(s)	Utilized for any task with a scheduling period of 1 year or more. The prefix or perform every $\underline{X}$ year would indicate the frequency (i.e. 1-Year would issue every 1 year).	Annual will be established as every 1 year

Figure 38: Frequency Assignment Examples

Scheduling Types

The scheduling type dictates how and when repetitive tasks will generate. There can up to three scheduling types associated with repetitive tasks; "fixed," "floating," and "duplicate or multiple." An important aspect to consider when establishing schedules is that all systems will determine the schedule start date based on the "next due date" or the "last date done" date. Identify which calculation your system uses to determine the ultimate issue date.

Fixed schedules maintain the established due date. For example, a monthly task is scheduled for generation on the 25th of each month. The fixed schedule maintains the 25th as the subsequent due date for all following months until a new due date is established. Fixed schedules are typically utilized for regulatory type tasks that must be accomplished at the identified frequency. A word of caution, some systems will not issue another scheduled task until the existing task has a status of "complete". If this task becomes buried within the backlog and forgotten, it will not come out again.

Floating schedules maintain the frequency but change the due date based on the completion date of the task. Using the same example above, the monthly task is scheduled for generation on the 25th and is completed on the 28th, so the next generation date would be the 28th. Floating schedules are typically utilized when a meter reading triggers the generation of the task (e.g., every 3,000 miles). If you have conducted load leveling of your repetitive tasks (a known and equal amount weekly or monthly), using this scheduling type will constantly change the levels established.

Many systems utilize a feature called duplicates or multiples. This feature will trigger the system to generate at the established frequency regardless if the previous task has been completed or not. This feature should be utilized to ensure repetitive tasks that are incomplete regenerate again and do not become forgotten buried in the maintenance backlog.

Routes

A route is a list of related equipment or assets that can be considered stops along the route. These route stops can be equipment, assets, locations, or a combination of them. A route can be as simple as an asset list identified for inspections. You can also create a route that identifies assets that are related by location, for example all of the servers in a computer lab, or by type of asset, such as all fire extinguishers located throughout the site. You can also define a sequence to indicate stops that should be inspected in a certain order. The utilization of routes is highly recommended to reduce travel time, which adds more efficiency to maintenance activities.

Reporting and Analysis

Every system has reporting and analysis capabilities to some level. These capabilities vary from system to system. While some are limited in predefined or "canned" reports, others contain the capability to develop user configurable reports and are only limited by the imagination of the user. While on the surface the "only limited by imagination" sounds good, all that creativity can be dangerous. I am a firm believer in establishing standard reports for an organization and using the standards for the basis of reporting information. This ensures everyone is looking at the same information, from the same data fields, presented in the same way every time. Numerous report writing tools are commercially available for systems that do not provide sufficient embedded reporting capabilities.

Some systems utilize templates to report Key Performance Indicator (KPI) information. These templates allow you to define what the calculation is, where the inputs come from, and the frequency at which to calculate the indicator. These KPIs can be displayed as dashboards that enable multiple KPIs to be grouped together and allow for quick analysis of the presented information.

Most systems have query, sometimes called "adhoc," capabilities that allow a user to define parameters to search, sort, segregate, and display data. These types of reports are useful for detailed analysis. The following are some recommended reports or queries:

Report or Query	Measures
PM Compliance	PMs completed / PMs scheduled
PM Delinquency	Delinquent PMs by date and equipment
Schedule Compliance (Volume)	Work orders completed / Work orders scheduled
Schedule Compliance (Performance)	Man-hours required / Man-hours scheduled
Scheduling Efficiency	Man-hours scheduled / Man-hours available
Work By Work Order Type	Completed or closed work orders by work order type (specify date range)
Work Order By Work Order Status	All work orders sorted or grouped by work order status
Total Maintenance Backlog	All open work orders sorted by crafts
Ready Maintenance Backlog	All open work orders with a status of ready or does not have a status of hold
Total Inventory Value	Total dollar value of all items in stock
Monthly Parts Usage	Total dollar value of all items issued (by month)
Materials Stock-outs	Parts available / Parts requested (stocked items only)
Maintenance Labor Costs	All closed work orders by work and equipment (specify date range)
Contractor Costs	All contractor costs by work, equipment, and area (specify date range)
Total Maintenance Cost	All costs for labor (internal/external), parts, or materials by equipment and area (specify date range)

Figure 39: Reports and Query Examples

With more organizations relying on contract maintenance support, ensure standard reports are developed to monitor their performance. The key to ensuring this information is reportable is to make sure all work performed is captured with a work order, identify them as the craft performing the work (landscaping contractor, HVAC contractor, etc. or by company name such as ABC-HVAC or ABC-Landscaping), utilize the correct work order type and class, and note the correct equipment or location where the work was performed. From this you can quickly see what an activity or activities cost, manpower expended (number of workers and time), and where the work was performed (equipment or location). Apply the same rule for contractors as you do for internal maintenance performing activities at your site: no work order, no event or activity took place.

System Changes after Implementation

Although I'm sure you have implemented your system flawlessly, there will be a time when system configuration changes will be requested by users.

A process must be defined to evaluate and implement necessary changes to fields or tables. Figure 40 shows the basic steps for establishing a system change process. Ensure there is an established review, approval process, and a need for the change.

While some changes on the surface may seem simple, there is always the potential for much more work than anticipated. Additionally, defined standard reports, KPI dashboards, and metrics may have to be reestablished to include the requested data. The system SOP document must be updated with the change information then determine training requirements or communicate the changes to the users.

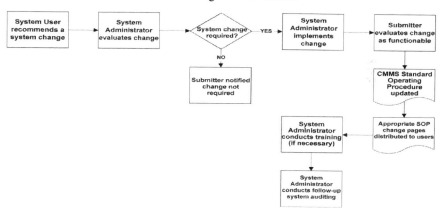

Figure 40: System Table or Field Configuration Change Process

System Administration

An assumption made by many is that the function of the system administration is performed by Information Technology (IT). They should play a role in the administration of the system: by installing the software, establishing it on the network, and upgrading the software when updates are released.

Ideally, someone from the implementation core team who has been involved from the start of the implementation is given the responsibility of system administration. Depending on the system and staff size, this could initially be a full-time responsibility until all users are fully trained and auditing results show proper system utilization.

The System Administrator is directly responsible for the establishment and ongoing maintenance of the system procedures, security assignments, and the table/field configurations of the system. Additionally, the system administrator coordinates the daily operations of the system, provides training, conducts system auditing for proper utilization, and coaches/ mentors system users. The System Administrator is also responsible for ensuring the consistent application of the established standards identified in the CMMS Standard Operating Procedures document and keeping the document updated with any system configuration changes.

Common Terminology Used in Systems

System Terminology	Description
Action(s) Taken	A specific code established for actions taken to repair or restore equipment. Utilized on work orders to facilitate equipment repair, solutions development, and equipment analysis.
Alternate Vendor	An alternate or secondary vendor that supplies like inventory items or services but is not the primary or preferred vendor.
ASP	Application Service Provider, a system that is stored on the vendor's server and a portal is provided for site use. Eliminates the need for an on-site server and IT support.
Assets	Assets that have been identified (and may be maintained) that are contained within the CMMS (see equipment). Some organizations refer to these assets as "accounting assets," which are not considered maintainable, but the financial value and location is tracked within the system.
Auditing	Reviewing of a process or flow identifying opportunities for improvement and validating that established data standards were followed.
BOM	Bill of Materials, the identification of all items that are utilized in the assembly of equipment or assets. Necessary for the quick identification of required parts for planning and executing maintenance activities.
Cause(s)	A specific code established for a cause of equipment failures. Utilized on work orders to facilitate equipment repair, solutions development, and equipment analysis.
CMMS	Computerized Maintenance Management System
Configuration	The establishment within the system of all those standards defined during the implementation phase and documented in the Standard Operating Procedures document.
Craft(s)	The identification of maintenance crafts for work order assignment (i.e. Mechanical, Electrical, Millwright, Machinist, etc.).
Customization	Modifying existing system functionality or features to change the "out of the box" system configuration.
Dashboard(s)	Defined indicators or metrics that have a visual reference established for quick glance reporting (i.e. indicator is in the red, yellow, or green).

System Terminology	Description
Data Population	The physical population of data within fields, tables, or records contained in a system.
Duplicates or Multiples	A task scheduling type that duplicates the due date regardless of task completion. If the due date was the 20th and the activity was never completed, the following month on the 20th another is released.
EAM	Enterprise Asset Management, a system to manage equipment or assets across multiple departments in an organization.
Emergency Work Order	A quick entry work order specifically relating to an emergency or urgent condition. Allows for quick entry with minimal informational requirements.
Employee Code	A code developed to identify a specific individual for access and assignment of system activities.
Equipment (EQ)	Equipment that has been identified and maintained that is contained within the system.
Equipment Class	Assignment of an equipment/assets class category to a group like equipment or assets together. Works in conjunction with the equipment type (i.e. pump as the type, positive displacement as the class).
Equipment Criticality	A ranking value assigned to equipment or assets indicating its importance to the site, facility, or process.
Equipment Number (EQ. NO.)	A unique number assigned to establish a piece of equipment within a system.
Equipment Type (EQ Type)	Assignment of an equipment/assets category to group like equipment or assets together (i.e. pump, motor, conveyor, etc.).
ERP	Enterprise Resource Planning, a system that integrates all site applications for total business management from or within one system.
Factory Calendar	Utilized to establish exceptions when the site or facility is not operating (i.e. holidays).
Failure(s)	A specific code established to identify the failure of an equipment component. Utilized on work orders to facilitate equipment repair, solutions development, and equipment analysis.
FIFO	First In First Out, indicates that the first item entered is the first item used. Using this method provides near current costing information.
Fixed	A task scheduling type that fixes the date to a specific day. If the due date was the 20th and the completion was the 31st, the next due date would be the 20th of the following month.
Floating	A task scheduling type that floats the next due date based on the date last performed. If it was due on the 20th and completed on the 28th, the next due date is changed to the 28th of the following month.
Frequency	The interval that a task will be repetitively issued. Typically expressed in days, weeks, months, years, hours, miles, etc.
Functional Location	The specific identification of a location that has a defined function (i.e. a process area or line). Used in establishing an equipment hierarchy.
Hosted Application	A hosted application allows users to execute and operate a software application from the cloud. (See SaaS)

System Terminology	Description
Implementation	The defining phase to develop all pertinent data standards that ensure consistent data collection.
Implementation Core Team	A team of cross-functional individuals from a site or facility that will be implementing a CMMS.
In-Service	An indicator that a specific piece of equipment or asset is currently in service and may have repetitive tasks assigned.
Installation	The physical installation of a system on a server or work station. Void of any site data at this time.
Interface or Interfacing	The interfacing of one program to another (i.e. a CMMS and an external accounting system).
Inventory Class	Assignment of an inventory class category to group like inventory items together. Works in conjunction with the inventory type (i.e. bearing as the type, pillow block as the class).
Inventory Type	Assignment of an inventory category to group like inventory items together (i.e. bearing, belt, fuse, etc.).
Job Plans	A detailed plan to execute an activity that identifies the required steps and actions, tools, materials, and crafts. Typically residing in a library or reusable repository in a system.
Kitting	The collection and segregation of specific parts or materials that have been reserved to a work order for a planned and scheduled maintenance work activity.
LIFO	Last In First Out, indicates that the last item entered is used first and the costing of that last purchase is the costing for all like items in stock.
Linear Assets	Assets that are linear in nature, such as roads, sidewalks, rails, etc.
Location	The physical location of equipment or assets. May have multiple fields associated to amplify locating information.
Meter(s)	A device that records operating hours, cycles, or miles and may be interfaced with a CMMS or require manual entry.
Min/Max	A method of establishing inventory stocking levels so the minimum is never reached and the maximum is never exceeded.
Nameplates or Specifications	The manufacturer's information located on equipment or assets that gives specifications, such as horsepower, ratings, voltages, etc. Necessary for the development of BOM information and PM activities.
Nested or Shadowed Tasks	A tool to group repetitive tasks together for release as a single activity. Utilized when an activity has service requirements, such as an oil change is conducted at 3,000 miles, a tire rotation at 9,000 miles, at the 9,000 mile activity, the 3,000 mile activity is included.
Operating Status	An indicator applied to equipment or assets or inventory items to indicate in use, in repair, available spare, etc.
Originator	The specific individual that has entered a request for an activity (see requestor).
Parent-Child Relationship	The establishment of maintainable components to parent equipment (i.e. the gearbox and motor are the child of the conveyor).

System Terminology	Description
PdM	Predictive Maintenance activities that may include IR technology, oil analysis, thickness testing, etc.
PM	Preventive Maintenance activities that include cleaning, inspecting, adjusting, and lubricating.
PO	Purchase Order, an approved purchase requisition that authorizes the expenditure of funds.
Primary Vendor	The primary vendor that supplies inventory items and is typically the preferred vendor.
Query or Adhoc	The utilization of different data elements from various tables or fields within a system for analysis.
Re-implementation	The activity of successfully reestablishing an existing system.
Requestor	The individual that has requested an action: work request, purchase requisition, etc. (see originator).
RFI	Request for Information, a request for detailed information from a vendor or supplier for a system, service, or item.
RFP	Request for Proposal, a request for a proposal from a vendor or supplier for a system, services, or items.
RFQ	Request for Quotation, a request for a quote from a vendor or supplier for a system, services, or items.
ROI	Return on Investment, the benefit received or returned to the business for accomplishing the activity. Often thought of as a financial return, however, could be efficiency or effectiveness improvement resulting in a financial return.
Role	A defined user role within a CMMS. Utilized to establish system access for all like groups.
ROP	Reorder Points, a method of establishing inventory stocking levels based on known usage and forecasting future usage.
Routes	The identification of equipment in specific locations for logical assignment to work orders to perform maintenance activities.
SaaS	Software as a Service, cloud based system accessed through an internet web browser, requires a monthly or annual subscription.
Scheduling Exceptions	A method to increase or decrease employee availability. Some systems utilize this functionality for site exceptions also (see Factory Calendar).
Service Request	A request to have an activity accomplished. Once approved becomes a work order. (See work request)
Smart Numbering	A numbering scheme utilized that incorporates additional information with the equipment or asset number, such as department, location, or type of equipment.
Solution(s)	A code established to specific equipment types and classes that displays the failure, the cause, and a potential solution to assist in troubleshooting and resolving equipment failures.
SOP	Standard Operating Procedures, a document developed during implementation capturing all configuration decisions and system standards defined.

System Terminology	Description
Staging	The staging of kitted parts to a secure area for use in a planned and scheduled maintenance activity.
Statuses	The indication that further action or intervention is required, typically utilized in the work order and the purchasing functionality of a system.
System Security	The assignment of system access to individuals within a CMMS. Module or area, record, and field access can be established through hidden, read only, or full access.
Task	A repetitive activity that may or may not have an assigned frequency for system release. Some systems utilize this for PMs, tasks, or job plans.
UDF	User Defined Field, a free text field that lets the end user store data for future use or reuse.
UOI	Unit of Issue, utilized to define an issue quantity.
UOM	Unit of Measure, utilized to define a unit (i.e. box, carton, case, hour, etc.).
UOP	Unit of Purchase, utilized to define a purchase quantity.
Validation	The process of verifying all information within the system and the configuration of the site or facility.
W/O	Work Order, a record that identifies what must be done and where it must be accomplished. Utilized as the data collection record for all maintenance and equipment activity.
W/O Class	Work Order Class, further breakdown of the work order type to enable drill-down for analysis.
W/O Number	Work Order number, a unique number assigned to each work order to establish a permanent record and facilitate look-up and retrieval.
W/O Type	Work Order Type, the type of work being accomplished in the execution of activities. May contain maintenance and non-maintenance activities. Typical types are emergency, calibration, PM, meetings, training, etc.
W/R	Work Request, a request to have an activity accomplished. Once approved becomes a work order. (See service request)
Weighted Average	Weighted average is the calculation of the cost of the current inventory, plus the cost of the new purchase, divided by the quantity on hand.
Work Order Life-Cycle	The life (time) of a work order from creation to closure in a CMMS.
Work Order Priorities	A numerical number assignment indicating the priority or importance of the identified work. Utilized to support proactive maintenance planning and scheduling.
Workflow	A documented process in block format indicating start, action requirements, and a stopping point.
Wrench-time	Time spent executing an activity not to include preparation time or travel time, only hands on the equipment time.

Assessing Your System

Most organizations utilize a Computerized Maintenance Management System (CMMS) to assist them in managing their equipment/assets and the maintenance that is performed on those assets. Have you ever wondered if you are receiving the maximum value from your system? What does good look like, and how do you compare?

As one who conducts numerous system assessments, I have witnessed the good, the bad, and the ugly. The good news is if you fall into the bad or ugly category, it can be fixed.

To assist in evaluating where you are with your system, I will share aspects of the system assessment I perform when helping organizations. Break the system down into areas or components, and evaluate each of those areas or components. Regardless of the system you utilize, look at the functionality that each provides. All can be categorized into the following: Equipment/Assets, Employees, Work Order processing, Parts/Materials, PM/Task Procedures, Planning and Scheduling, History and Reporting, and Key Performance Indicators or Metrics.

Use the following ranking to score your findings:

Assigned Ranking	Point Value
Excellent (All items within the assessment were identified)	10
Very Good (A majority of the items within the assessment were identified)	9
Good (Most of the items within the assessment were identified)	8
Average (Some of the items within the assessment were identified)	7
Below Average (Few of the items within the assessment were identified)	6
Poor (None of the items within the assessment were identified)	5 or less

If your total score is **350** or below, you have significant opportunities for improvement. Additionally, if you share your findings with me, I will review them and provide comments on how to address the issues you have identified. Enjoy assessing.

Assessing Equipment/Assets

Functional Area	Conditions	Comments	Ranking
Equipment/Assets	Hierarchy structure is complete?	All maintainable equipment/ assets are contained with the system.	
Equipment/Assets	Parent/child relationships are established for all equipment/assets?	Each maintainable component (i.e. Motors, Gearboxes, etc.) is attached to its respective parent.	
Equipment/Assets	An equipment/asset numbering scheme is defined?	Utilizing a sequential number is preferred over developing smart numbering that identifies types, classes, or locations within the number.	
Equipment/Assets	All equipment/assets are quickly locatable by system users?	Capabilities to quickly identify the proper piece of equipment are critical to accurate data collection.	
Equipment/Assets	A defined process exists to add or remove equipment/ assets to the system?	A process must be defined to ensure the configuration of the site and of the system are always identical.	
Equipment/Assets	Locations can quickly be searched to identify which equipment/ assets are in specific locations to develop route maintenance?	To enable logical routes for execution of maintenance, activities locations should facilitate groups of all equipment within a specific location. Utilizing this approach reduces travel time.	
Equipment/Assets	The equipment/asset is tagged with the system equipment/asset number and description?	To ensure accurate data collection all equipment should be tagged to ensure the proper equipment is identified.	
Equipment/Assets	The equipment type and class facilitates are used for grouping of like items for BOM and procedural assignment?	Equipment types and classes should be utilized to group like equipment together (i.e. Centrifugal Pumps, AC Motors, DC Motors, etc.)	
Equipment/Assets	Equipment locations define the specific location where the item is physically located?	This location data is utilized to enable someone to navigate to the exact location of the equipment/asset.	
Equipment/Assets	Equipment criticality is assigned for each piece of equipment/asset?	This is a necessary requirement to ensure the most critical equipment/assets are addressed first.	

Assessing Employees/Contractors

Functional Area	Conditions	Comments	Ranking
Employees/Contractors	All employees that maintain equipment/ assets that are established?	All should be established to facilitate scheduling work orders, collecting hours, and costs expended.	
Employees/Contractors	Contractors are established and execute work through the work order system?	All who maintain equipment must be established to capture activities completed, hours, and costs expended.	
Employees/Contractors	No unnecessary personal information is contained within the system?	Social Security numbers should never be entered. Home addresses and personal contact information should only be visible to the System Administrator.	
Employees/Contractors	Each employee established has an hourly burden labor rate assigned?	Cost collection for maintenance decisions is critical. The burdened rate should be assigned to assist in accurately managing the maintenance budget.	
Employees/Contractors	Employee availability and schedules are developed?	To utilize the scheduling functionality of the system, availability must be known and schedules developed for each employee.	

Assessing Work Order Processing

Functional Area	Conditions	Comments	Ranking
Work Order Processing	Work order priorities are well defined and are utilized to identify mean time to respond?	These work order priorities work in conjunction with the equipment criticality. They assist in identifying the most important work on the most important equipment/assets.	
Work Order Processing	Mean time to approve, plan, schedule, and execute work orders is known and routinely measured?	The work management process should be monitored to make adjustments in the process; these measurements indicate where emphasis should be placed.	
Work Order Processing	Work order types clearly identify the types of work performed?	Some typical types would be PM, EMERGENCY, CALIBRATION, etc. Keep in mind that maintenance resources are utilized for as much non-maintenance work as maintenance work.	
Work Order Processing	Work order classes (if available) are utilized properly?	Work order classes help further define work order types. For example, PdM (Predictive Maintenance) as a work order type could have classes of IR, OIL ANALYSIS, VIBRATION ANALYSIS, etc. assigned.	
Work Order Processing	All work orders with a status of READY have crafts and estimated times assigned?	To accurately schedule the activity for completion, knowing which craft(s) must accomplish the activity and how long it will take must be identified.	
Work Order Processing	Age of the maintenance backlog is known? (Both total backlog and ready backlog)	The total backlog is all work orders with a status of READY or AWAITING PARTS by estimated craft hours expressed in man-weeks. The ready backlog is those work orders with a status of READY by estimated craft hours expressed in man-weeks. This can be further broken down by specific craft (i.e. Mechanical, Electrical, etc.)	
Work Order Processing	Work order audits are routinely performed?	Periodic auditing of the work order process will identify opportunities for improvement. Audits should start with the originator and follow the work order through its life cycle (creation to closure) to identify potential areas of improvement.	

Functional Area	Conditions	Comments	Ranking
Work Order Processing	Work order statuses clearly identify where a work order is in its life cycle?	Work order statuses drive the work order through the system, They identify by role what actions are required to move the work order from creation to closure.	
Work Order Processing	Work management processes and flows are developed and trained to the organization?	These processes and flows represent the organization's ways of accomplishing work. They work in conjunction with the work order statuses to approve, plan, schedule, and execute work within a defined process.	

Assessing Parts and Materials

Functional Area	Conditions	Comments	Ranking
Parts and Materials	All parts and materials within the storeroom/ warehouse are established within the system?	All items utilized in maintaining and repairing equipment/assets must be within the system to accurately capture material usage and cost.	
Parts and Materials	Accurate costing information is established for each item within the system?	Accurate costing information is necessary to understand the true cost of repairing and maintaining equipment/assets. Cost savings opportunities could be identified for bulk or global purchases of items.	
Parts and Materials	Items requiring shelf life monitoring are established?	All items do not last forever; items that have a shelf life should be monitored within the system and should not be issued after the expiration date. Drive belts and rubber based products should be date stamped when received and evaluated after 3 years.	
Parts and Materials	Bills of Materials (BOM) are developed?	Bills of Materials specify all items (parts/components) that were utilized in the manufacturing of the equipment/asset. They should include both stocked and non-stocked items. Establishing them saves significant research time when planning work and identifying necessary parts/materials.	
Parts and Materials	Item descriptions are standardized?	Standardized descriptions are necessary to facilitate searches and sorts for quick identification of necessary items. The noun, verb, and adjective approach is typically utilized (i.e. BEARING, PILLOW BLOCK, 1-3/4 INCH).	
Parts and Materials	Item types and classes facilitate quick search and sort capabilities for the end user?	Item types and classes facilitate grouping and sorting of like items. Not all systems provide both types and classes, so care must be taken when establishing types if class is not available. Example of type and class would be BEARING (type) PILLOW BLOCK (class). If only type is available, the same bearing would be entered as BEARING-PB. Ensure the character limitations for the fields are fully understood before defining types and classes.	

Assessing Tasks/Procedures

Functional Area	Conditions	Comments	Ranking
PM Tasks/Procedures	Master tasks or procedures are utilized?	The utilization of master tasks or procedures is recommended. For example, a motor inspection task would be created and utilized on all like motors. This saves significant time when a change in the procedure is necessary (i.e. change it one time and all places where it is utilized change). Might want to revisit your equipment types to assist in identifying opportunities for master task/procedure assignments.	
PM Tasks/Procedures	Assigned frequencies for execution are appropriate for the activity?	Unfortunately, many organizations never review the PM's or the frequencies performed. They merely do what they have always done. Start by looking at work order history and see which ones have been missed, then see if there have been any failures. These would be candidates to change the frequency. Keep in mind lubrication and regulatory tasks/procedures should not be changed.	
PM Tasks/Procedures	Correct task/procedure scheduling type is utilized?	Many systems have multiple scheduling types to release tasks/procedures. It is imperative you understand each type and utilize the correct type for your organization. Some types will not release the next task until the previous one has been completed. Some change the next scheduled due date based on when the existing one was completed, and another releases regardless of the disposition of the current one (did not complete this month another automatically issues next month). There are inherent dangers with each one, so choose wisely.	

Assessing Tasks/Procedures

Functional Area	Conditions	Comments	Ranking
PM Tasks/Procedures	Task/procedure naming conventions facilitate quick searching and grouping for re-use?	The purpose of developing tasks/procedures is to identify activities that are performed repetitively for quick use to reduce mean time to plan work. Descriptive names facilitate quick look-up and identification of required tasks for release.	
PM Tasks/Procedures	Each task/procedure has a craft and estimated time to complete the activity assigned?	All tasks/procedures must have a craft(s) identified and the estimated time to complete the activity. The goal is a reduction of mean time to schedule activities.	

Assessing Planning and Scheduling

Functional Area	Conditions	Comments	Ranking
Planning and Scheduling	Work schedules are available for each Supervisor showing the work orders assigned to their direct reports?	Although Supervisors are responsible for their direct reports, many do not have schedules to assist them on where they are or what they are working on. The typical day-to-day direction for many maintenance resources comes from radio calls or direct contact from those having issues throughout the site. To effectively measure schedule compliance, all scheduled and those who supervise should have a copy of the schedule.	
Planning and Scheduling	Daily and weekly schedules are provided to all maintenance resources that have scheduled work?	It has been proven hundreds of times that if people are given schedules, they understand the expectations for the scheduling period and make every attempt to meet those expectations.	
Planning and Scheduling	Schedule compliance is measured?	If schedules are developed, it only makes sense to measure schedule compliancy. Did we do what we said we were going to do? If not, why? Some organizations measure schedule compliance daily and others weekly.	
Planning and Scheduling	100% of each maintenance resource's available time is scheduled?	Many organizations "hold-back" some time just in case something happens. What if nothing happens that day and more schedule work could have been accomplished? Through the planning effort, interruptible work could be scheduled for emergency or urgent response.	
Planning and Scheduling	Daily maintenance resources non-available time is known?	Equally important as the available time is the time resources are not available. To ensure schedules developed are realistic and achievable, both available and unavailable time must be understood. Something as simple as an annual hearing test could have a significant impact. The test takes 30-minutes to accomplish; however, there are 20 maintenance resources for a loss of 10-hours that day.	

Assessing History and Reporting

Functional Area	Conditions	Comments	Ranking
History and Reporting	Historical equipment/ asset reviews are routinely conducted?	Routine reviews should be conducted on the history of equipment/assets to identify repetitive failures, mean time between failures, and abnormal expenditures of labor hours or parts and materials. These reviews should be conduct monthly.	
History and Reporting	Standard maintenance management reports are developed?	Standard reports should be developed for the organization and all use the established standards for the basis of reporting information. This ensures everyone is looking at the same information, from the same data fields, and it is presented the same way every time.	
History and Reporting	PM compliance is measured, monitored, and reported?	Since Preventive Maintenance (PM) work is considered the most important work maintenance can accomplish, compliance must be measured. This information should be utilized to determine the success of the program and the basis for changing frequencies for executing or not executing the PM.	
History and Reporting	Adhoc queries are never utilized as standard reports?	Queries are excellent tools to drill down and identify problem areas but should never be utilized as standard reports. Data manipulation is possible in queries and incorrect conclusions could be made.	
History and Reporting	Inventory usage reviews are routinely conducted?	Parts and materials utilized should be reviewed monthly at a minimum to ensure stock levels, min/max, or reorder points are established correctly: where used is understood, and validation of BOM information is performed.	

Assessing KPI's/Metrics

Functional Area	Conditions	Comments	Ranking
KPI's/Metrics	Meaningful KPI's/ metrics are defined?	These are the report cards for the organization. One must understand the difference between leading indicators/metrics (predicts the future) and lagging indicators/ metrics (it has happened). A combination of both is required as well as others that assist in managing the business. Ensure you measure what you treasure.	
KPI's/Metrics	The organization has been trained on the utilization of the established KPI's/ metrics?	Having measures is good; however, having measures that everyone understands is better. It is best if each role understands not only the measure but how they impact that measure.	
KPI's/Metrics	Current KPI's/ metrics are posted for the entire organization to see?	Measures should be viewed as behavior drivers. So if the measures aren't posted for all to see, how can behavior be driven?	
KPI's/Metrics	KPI/metrics dashboards are developed for quick visual reference?	Dashboards are good visual measure for all to see and quickly intervene when necessary.	
KPI's/Metrics	KPI's/metrics are utilized by the organization to drive appropriate behaviors?	If these measures are not utilized to drive the appropriate behaviors, one has to question why perform the measure? Additionally, if there is a perception that this information is used for personal performance measures, realistic information will not be collected.	

About the Author

Dave Bertolini is a Managing Principal for People and Processes, Inc., a firm that specializes in changing cultures from reactive to proactive through the optimization of people and processes. He has more than thirty-five years' experience in improvement initiatives. His experience includes twenty years in Naval Aviation, during which he built a solid foundation of training principles in support of operations, maintenance, and mission objectives as a P-3 Orion flight-crew member.

His certification as a Reliability Leader, Master Instructor, and Seminar Leader has led to his involvement in over three hundred and seventy-five improvement initiatives and CMMS implementations, utilizing thirty-nine different software packages. He has conducted numerous CMMS needs analyses and CMMS selections for facilities, municipalities, and manufacturing environments. In addition, he routinely conducts educational seminars on CMMS selection, Request for Proposal (RFP) development and avoiding CMMS implementation failures. He routinely is a speaker at the CMMS/EAM Conference and the International Maintenance Conference and has numerous articles published in trade publications for facilities, municipalities, and manufacturing plants.

His satisfied clients include Alcatel-Lucent, Procter & Gamble, Motorola, Uniroyal, DirecTV, Ainsworth Engineered, Lockheed Martin, City of Akron, City of South Bend, Old World Industries, Ohio State University, J.M. Huber Corporation, Rayonier, Cornell University, Georgia-Pacific, Northrop Grumman Corporation, PCS Phosphate White Springs, C. H. Guenther & Son Inc., Trinity Industries, and Latrobe Specialty Metals.

Questions about this book can be sent to:
dbertolini@peopleandprocesses.com or **david.bertolini@yahoo.com**

Uptime® Elements

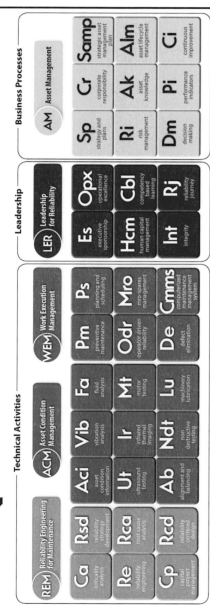

A Reliability Framework and Asset Management System™

Technical Activities

(REM) Reliability Engineering for Maintenance

Ca critically analysis	Rsd reliability strategy development
Re reliability engineering	Rca root cause analysis
Cp capital project management	Rcd reliability centered design

(ACM) Asset Condition Management

Aci asset condition information	Vib vibration analysis	Fa fluid analysis
Ut ultrasound testing	Ir infrared thermal imaging	Mt motor testing
Ab alignment and balancing	Ndt non destructive testing	Lu machinery lubrication

(WEM) Work Execution Management

Pm preventive maintenance	Ps planning and scheduling
Odr operator driven reliability	Mro mro-spares management
De defect elimination	Cmms computerized maintenance management system

Leadership

(LER) Leadership for Reliability

Es executive sponsorship	Opx operational excellence
Hcm human capital management	Cbl competency based learning
Int integrity	Rj reliability journey

Business Processes

(AM) Asset Management

Sp strategy and plans	Cr corporate responsibility	Samp strategic asset management plan
Ri risk management	Ak asset knowledge	Alm asset lifecycle management
Dm decision making	Pi performance indicators	Ci continuous improvement

A Reliability Framework and Asset Management System™

Reliabilityweb.com's Asset Management Timeline

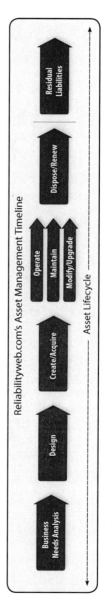

Business Needs Analysis → Design → Create/Acquire → Operate / Maintain / Modify/Upgrade → Dispose/Renew → Residual Liabilities

Asset Lifecycle

reliabilityweb.com • maintenance.org • reliabilityleadership.com

Reliabilityweb.com® and Uptime® Magazine Mission: **To make the people we serve safer and more successful.** One way we support this mission is to suggest a reliability system for asset performance management as pictured above. Our use of the Uptime Elements is designed to assist you in categorizing and organizing your own Body of Knowledge (BoK) whether it be through training, articles, books or webinars. Our hope is to make YOU safer and more successful.

ABOUT RELIABILITYWEB.COM

Created in 1999, Reliabilityweb.com provides educational information and peer-to-peer networking opportunities that enable safe and effective reliability and asset management for organizations around the world.

ACTIVITIES INCLUDE:

Reliabilityweb.com® (www.reliabilityweb.com) includes educational articles, tips, video presentations, an industry event calendar and industry news. Updates are available through free email subscriptions and RSS feeds. **Confiabilidad.net** is a mirror site that is available in Spanish at www.confiabilidad.net.

Uptime® Magazine (www.uptimemagazine.com) is a bi-monthly magazine launched in 2005 that is highly prized by the reliability and asset management community. Editions are obtainable in both print and digital.

Reliability Leadership Institute® Conferences and Training Events (www.reliabilityleadership.com) offer events that range from

unique, focused-training workshops and seminars to small focused conferences to large industry-wide events, including the International Maintenance Conference (IMC), MaximoWorld and The RELIABILITY Conference™ (TRC).

MRO-Zone Bookstore (www.mro-zone.com) is an online bookstore offering

a reliability and asset management focused library of books, DVDs and CDs published by Reliabilityweb.com.

Association of Asset Management Professionals

(www.maintenance.org) is a member organization and online community that encourages professional development and certification and supports information exchange and learning with 50,000+ members worldwide.

A Word About Social Good

Reliabilityweb.com is mission-driven to deliver value and social good to the reliability and asset management communities. *Doing good work and making profit is not inconsistent*, and as a result of Reliabilityweb.com's mission-driven focus, financial stability and success has been the outcome. For over a decade, Reliabilityweb.com's positive contributions and commitment to the reliability and asset management communities have been unmatched.

Other Causes

Reliabilityweb.com has financially contributed to include industry associations, such as SMRP, AFE, STLE, ASME and ASTM, and community charities, including the Salvation Army, American Red Cross, Wounded Warrior Project, Paralyzed Veterans of America and the Autism Society of America. In addition, we are proud supporters of our U.S. Troops and first responders who protect our freedoms and way of life. That is only possible by being a for-profit company that pays taxes.

I hope you will get involved with and explore the many resources that are available to you through the Reliabilityweb.com network.

Warmest regards,
Terrence O'Hanlon
CEO, Reliabilityweb.com